When he was sixteen he had big muscles
and was tan all over from swimming
in the nude. There was a reason why
lecherous old ladies ordered from
Adams' Grocery.
The Boy delivered more than food – and
he provided services you couldn't buy
in any store…

THE GIRL

When she was fourteen, men lusted after
her. They thought she was the prettiest
little girl that ever laid foot to ground.
They would pay for her favours, she was
so pretty. And she was happy to have
found out the one secret a lot of women
never learned: that when a man really
wanted something he would give just
about anything to get it…

Also in Arrow by Anonymous

HER
HIM
THEM

ME

BY ANONYMOUS

ARROW BOOKS

Arrow Books Limited
17–21 Conway Street, London W1P 6JD

An imprint of the
Hutchinson Publishing Group

London Melbourne Sydney Auckland
Johannesburg and agencies
throughout the world

First published in Great Britain 1982
By arrangement with Bantam Books
Reprinted 1982

Made and printed in Great Britain
by The Anchor Press Ltd
Tiptree, Essex
ISBN 0 09 927380 2

for the last time:
for HER

Author's Preface

It seems to me that, in these recent years since the censorship bars have been lowered, the language of love, following Gresham's Law, has been debased into a coarse coinage, with neither tenderness nor love—nor, indeed, any true emotion at all.

It has been my ardent desire to new-mint these words, this language, by writing them in the context in which they are most often spoken. For this, the earthy language of love, is the best and truest tongue in the world. There has been, in literature, a separation between the word and the deed. I have tried to unite them again.

It has been my intention to arouse my reader, not by the scenes and events of the book but by his own particular remembrance. I want him to recollect in tranquillity those great times when, clasped by a woman's arms and legs, a voice has breathed into his ear, "Fuck me. Oh God, fuck me." I want the woman *reader to recollect in tranquillity those times she has been compelled to utter those words. I want them both to remember how beautiful and true was the language of their passion, because, in the moment of love, they were the only words that would do. I want my reader to remember those brief moments in which he has loved and tasted every pore of a lover's body, when a lover has tasted every sensuous inch of his own. And I want the lovers to know, all over again, that at such times a man is never more a man, a woman never more a woman, and that they are joined into a meaning infinitely greater than the sum of their parts, for their coupling is an equation of love.*

Why do we debase these lovely words? Because we are ashamed of their true emotional meaning, we are afraid to open our souls and our bodies, as these words demand that they be opened. Love is an openness.

The above manifesto signaled the publication of the novel *Her*, by Anonymous. Since that memorable occasion, I have continued to explore the areas of possibilities within the scope of this manifesto, in successive novels entitled *Him, Us, You . . .* and now *Me*. These novels have found a readership numbered in the millions, and I trust they will continue to do so as long as the publisher keeps them in print.

Now, with the publication of *Me*—this story of twin Candides let loose in our modern world—I think I have done it. I believe I have fulfilled the principles of the manifesto; and I believe that the readers of these novels have, by virtue of their very numbers, accepted with equal honesty of belief these enunciated principles.

So Anonymous will now disappear, returning into that deep part of myself from which he, or she, emerged to write these books, for the task is now finished. I will not venture to predict it, but it may be that in some as yet unrealized future he/she will emerge again, in another guise, with another manifesto to promulgate in the written word.

But for now, dear readers in your millions, that's all there is: five novels, each complete within itself and yet each forming a part of a linked whole for those perceptive enough, open enough, to divine the linkages; and it is my fondest hope that they will live forever, as, I believe, they deserve to live, in the minds and thoughts and feelings of new readers, and of old readers returning to confirm and resavor an old delight.

I, Anonymous, have found great fulfillment in writing these books, and perhaps an even greater delight in watching unseen the enormous success they have enjoyed. On numerous occasions I have heard these novels discussed, praised or condemned, considered seriously or dismissed out-of-hand. My own critical opinion has been solicited, to my secret pleasure, though I have always suppressed the impulse to proselytize in my own anonymous behalf.

So I, as my real self, am deeply grateful to Anonymous for emerging so unexpectedly from the depths of me . . . and for remaining long enough to write these books. I am grateful to my publishers— who have never been privy to my true identity—for their courage in publishing them, in keeping them on the stands in one printing after another, and for their refusal to exploit them cheaply but, rather, presenting them in discreet and dignified formats worthy of the intent of the text.

But, most of all, I am deeply grateful to the millions of readers who have granted to these books their time and attention, who have reveled in them, reread them, recommended them to their friends and lovers, who have, indeed, kept them alive. And will, I fervently hope, continue to do so.

And so, fondly, and sadly, Anonymous bids you

farewell. But he/she leaves behind this legacy, five novels, each written in "the earthy language of love . . . the best and truest tongue in the world." These five:

Her
Him
Us
You
I

ANONYMOUS

Me

The Boy

I ain't no stud. Ain't *never* been no stud, no matter what anybody might tell you. Them old ladies ain't my fault; what else is a fellow going to do?

Now, take when I was sixteen years old, and delivering groceries for Old Man Adams' store, there in Pass Robin where I was born and raised to be a man. Pass Robin is on the Gulf Coast, so there's just two kinds of people, the folks who run the stores and do the commercial fishing and just live in Pass Robin because that was where they was born; then there's the other kind, with summer houses that have been in the same family, sometimes, since before the Civil War. They come from all over the southern states, and even as far away as Chicago and New York City in the summertime, and go away in the fall.

It's them kind of old ladies I'm talking about. They ordered their groceries by telephone instead of making a trip to the store, and they liked to have me de-

1

liver their order. I liked to do the delivering because, over and above what Old Man Adams paid me, sometimes I'd get as much as a dollar from one old lady or another.

So I couldn't help it. Let me just give you an idea of what went on that summer I was sixteen years old and just coming to be a man. You'll see what I mean.

Take a Thursday. That was always a big day for grocery deliveries, because everybody stocked up for the weekend, you understand, maybe even for weekend guests, because these old ladies were mighty big on having visitors come to see them in Pass Robin. I drove a pickup truck with a cover on it to keep off the sun, and a big ice chest to keep the meat and milk fresh. Early in the morning I'd set out on my route down the beach roads, and sometimes I wouldn't get back to the store before twelve o'clock noon.

Now, this particular Thursday. First stop was a house hadn't been open until now; first time this year I had delivered an order here. The driveway around to the back of the house—I always delivered at the kitchen door—was still full of tall weeds, and I could hear them dragging on the underside of the pickup. It was one of our pretty Gulf Coast mornings, a day when a fellow'd a lot rather be out on a sailboat, or gone fishing, than making his living working for Old Man Adams. It *was* making a living for me, too, not just pocket money, because my daddy hadn't worked in so long I couldn't remember when he had struck the last lick, and Mama was so down in the back most of the time she couldn't take in much washing and ironing.

Pretty morning. Driving along the beach road, I could see the high wisps of clouds tailing northeast—being pushed by a strong wind up there, you see—and out in the channel a commercial boat coming in, its old motor chugging faithfully. An osprey flew low

2

with flapping wings, carrying a big fish in its claws, and one or two gulls whirled up, begging him to drop it so they'd have a chance.

I had the habit of noticing that sort of thing, along with the smells of a low tide, and musky odors of the night-blooming things, growing fainter now by the heat of the coming sun. It's at times like that I wished Billy was along with me, because he always taken an enjoyment in such good things. Billy was my twin brother who got sick of a fever and died when me and him was nine years old. Ain't never been nobody in this world like unto Billy. We had looked so much alike that folks couldn't tell us apart, so we used to play games even on Mama and Daddy about which was which.

The important thing about me and Billy, though, was not how much we looked alike, but that our heads worked together. He couldn't think a thought without me knowing it, or vice versa. Didn't even have to talk much, just glance at the other fellow and know he was going to say, "Let's go fishing," or, "Them muscadines are probably ripe by now, we ought to check 'em out," or, "The answer is ninety-eight and a half, idiot."

Didn't nobody know it but him and me, but he was the fellow who always noticed how things looked and felt and smelled, and could even draw them down on paper, whilst I was the fellow who did all the fistfighting when it come necessary, because Billy didn't like to put his strength onto another boy, not if he could help it. Just softhearted, that was all.

The world has been only half a world since Billy took sick of the fever and died when me and him was nine years old; though I do try to pay attention to what he used to see in the course of a day's living. It's like I've got to keep up his end as well as my own, now that he's passed away and can't do it himself. Folks thought I was a hardhearted boy because I didn't seem to grieve for my twin brother, crying and carrying on at the funeral like some folks do to let everybody know what a great loss they are suffering. Little do they know. It's not easy to live in just a piece of the world when you used to know it whole.

It was on mornings like this that I could best feel Billy traveling with me, not to be seen, but there, right on. Somewhere above my left shoulder, because if folks had known the secret that I stood or walked or sat always to the right, while he stood or walked or sat always to the left, they wouldn't have had any trouble telling us apart.

At this first house, I knocked loud on the screen door and called out, "Grocery boy." Then I went right on in, because the people are often down on the beach, or still sleeping, or just too summer-lazy to pay attention to a delivery boy. I do the job right, too, putting the meat and milk and ice cream, if any, into the refrigerator instead of just dumping everything on the kitchen table without a thought or a care.

That, in fact, was what I was busy doing when this old lady said, "Well, good morning."

I turned around to speak my polite reply. And I knew right then, at first look.

Now, like I said, I ain't no stud. Never have been. But I *know*. I don't know how it is that I know, but you just take an old lady and put a thought into her head, and I can read it like a book. Even when she hasn't got around as yet to recognizing the thought herself.

For one thing, this particular old lady didn't have anything on under the flimsy robe she was wearing. Of course, in the heat of a Gulf Coast summer, a person doesn't want to be going around in a heavy bathrobe. But still and all . . .

This one wasn't bad-looking for an old lady. She had black hair and black eyes, and she didn't need to put her face on of a morning, like so many do. The

4

white thing she was wearing was cut down practically to her navel, and I could see the nipples of her breasts through it. They were standing up, as rosy as an apple. But I already knew before I looked at the nipples.

"Good morning," I said. "Grocery boy."

She laughed, a low and throaty sound. "I didn't think you were the neighborhood rapist."

I shut the door of the refrigerator. "Want me to put up the canned stuff for you?" I asked.

"That would be nice."

Her eyes followed me as I moved back and forth across the kitchen floor, sorting out the cans into the shelves according to what was already there. For a while she didn't say anything. But it hadn't gone away; if anything, it had got heavier.

"How old are you?" she asked after the silence had got to be noticeable.

"Eighteen," I said. I always lied two years' worth, because nobody wanted to believe I was only sixteen.

"You're big for your age," she said.

"Yes'm," I said. "I've always been like that."

"Always?" she said teasingly. "Even when you were a little boy?"

Always. Just born to grow plenty of muscle, I reckon. It's not that I'm all that tall, but I'm broad, with strong arms and legs and wide shoulders and a waist as small as a girl's.

"I've always liked blond hair and blue eyes," she said. "Even your eyebrows are white."

"That's from the sun, I reckon," I said, feeling embarrassed like I always did when they got to talking about me as though I wasn't really there at all.

She chuckled, the low and throaty sound again. "I'll bet you've got pretty girls running after you all the time."

Now, why is it that, when an old lady gets the thought into her head, she always starts in on how

5

many girls you got? Ain't never had no girlfriend; I never know how to act around girls.

"Well, ma'am, I'm always busy working, I guess," I said, ducking my head.

"A strong boy like you, and so handsome?" she said scoffingly. "Come here and let me feel your muscle."

I looked at her from all the way across the kitchen. She was sitting on the edge of the table now. Her legs were open, like she didn't know what was showing, you understand. And the nipples were bigger now, like two thumbs underneath the flimsy fabric.

I walked toward her, my hands reaching for the next stack of canned goods. She put both hands around my upper arm, bare under the short-sleeved shirt, and I could feel how damp her palms were.

"See, I can't even reach around your muscles with both hands," she said, a tremble in her voice.

Loosening her grip, she stroked my arm. "Your skin is as soft as a baby's skin."

I stood still, letting her touch me. They always want to touch you. And while she stroked my arm, my mind was feeling for her mind, so that I would know how to do. I always need to know how it is with them, you understand, because you can't help but feel sorry for an old lady like that. They are so needful.

"I'll bet you're tan all over," she said. "Are you tanned all over?"

"Well, yes'm," I said. "We always go out to the little islands to go swimming, where a fellow don't need to wear a bathing suit."

The deep laugh again. "I knew it. I can tell, you know. I can just look at a man, and . . ."

"You want me to put up the rest of the groceries?" I said.

She drew in a sharp breath and took her hands from my arm. "Yes. Of course."

6

I picked up both hands full of cans and walked across the floor to the shelves. I put them up carefully, one by one. Then I turned to look at her again, and this time I knew how it had to be, knew it just as well as if she had told me in so many words.

She was still sitting on the kitchen table. Her legs were open, and I could see that she had red hair there, not black, like on top of her head. I could hear her breathing all the way across the room. So I reached down and unzipped my pants.

"Oh, Lord, yes," she said when she saw Him.

I started walking Him across the floor to her, her legs lifting and opening, and when I came between them, they were high enough to circle around my waist and clamp the heels into the small of my back. Which pushed Him right into her, deep and true, and I felt the sigh of her body, the strength of her hands clutching at my shoulders to hold herself closer.

"Oh, you are big for your age, aren't you?" she whispered, holding me tight against her. Then her voice changed; it got angry as she said, "Don't move."

I didn't move. I just stood there, feeling the trembling in her body, deep and shaking, shuddering her flesh. And then I could feel the ripples growing inside her, rippling and rippling and rippling, because she was moving now, not on the outside, but completely on the inside; and because I knew it was the way she wanted it, I held myself still and let her have her way.

Her hands were like claws on my shoulders now, and she was breathing hard, her lower lip bitten so hard between her teeth that I thought it would draw blood. She was staring into my eyes like a bird will stare at a snake, and she was saying, "Big, oh, yes, how can it be so big, so big, so . . ."

It started then, just standing still like that, because she was doing it all; she knew it was starting. I saw the change come into her eyes, and she started too, the rippling strong and fierce now, and her hips

7

were thrusting and thrusting, and then it grew and grew and grew, and when it burst she let out a cry like a cat.

We stood together for a time, her legs still around me, holding Him in her. I wanted to move, but because she didn't want me to leave her yet, I stayed there until she gave me the signal by taking her legs from around my waist. And all the time, I was looking into her eyes, watching the memory of Him washing through them, then ebbing, then washing through them again. And I knew that I had done good.

I finished putting up the groceries while she sat silently watching. We didn't say anything. Then she said, "Well! I don't know what got into me."

I turned to look at her, and she was just an old lady again. "I'm sorry, ma'am," I said, knowing it was what she wanted to hear.

She laughed nervously. "You can at least quit calling me 'ma'am' now."

"I don't know your name," I said.

"It's Sally," she said. "Will you call me Sally?"

"Yes, ma'am, Miss Sally," I said.

She was still looking at me as if she didn't believe I had happened in her kitchen this morning. "How old did you say you were?"

"Eighteen," I said, because no old lady ever wanted to believe I was sixteen.

She had to make light of eighteen, even. "You could have fooled me," she said, making a laugh along with it. She hesitated. "I hope you won't go around talking about me . . . bragging. . . ."

"Oh, no, ma'am," I told her truthfully. "I don't ever talk about any of my good customers."

She looked at me sharply. "You sound like you're . . . rather used to this sort of thing."

"I've got some nice customers," I said. I didn't want to keep talking about it, so I said, "I've got to go now. A lot of deliveries to make yet."

She slid off the table. "I suppose I owe you a tip for . . . for delivering the groceries. Wait a minute."

"You don't have to tip me," I said politely. "It's a service of the store that we are proud to provide to our steady customers."

She was easier with the laughter this time. "You do provide service, I have to admit that," she said. "Wait a minute."

I waited while she disappeared into the house, thinking that I knew the kitchens but rarely had I been invited into the rest of the house. Well, that was how I liked it; it don't do to get too easy with people you do a service for, like delivering groceries.

She came back and handed me a five-dollar bill. I stood holding it. "That's too much," I said.

She put her hand on the side of my head, brushing back the long hair there with a quick, warm gesture that made me afraid I'd be further delayed. I was already thinking about old lady Brandon on down the road, how she'd be peeping and peering out the kitchen door wondering why I was so late in coming.

"A hundred dollars wouldn't be too much," she said, the throatiness in her voice again, so that I moved a step away. I didn't want her to keep on touching me. "You deliver all the time, don't you?"

"Yes, ma'am, Miss Sally," I said. "Anytime you phone in an order of groceries, I got to bring them out."

She nodded thoughtfully. "That's good to know."

That's how it came to be with her, starting the same and ending the same and staying the same in between, as though each delivery was the very first. That's just how it is; every old lady I ever knew had her own ways, and if a fellow wants to make them happy, he must let them use their little ways just as they wish.

So I went on, hustling, because, not having

counted on Miss Sally, I was running behind schedule, and I never did like to answer questions about how come I was late today. Each old lady was a separateness unto herself, you see, so that I never let one know about the others.

Five or six houses with lots of people in them, families and visitors, so that it was an hour before I got to old lady Brandon's house. The kitchen was empty. I made noise opening and slamming the door of the refrigerator, clattering the cupboard doors as I put up the canned goods. The kitchen stayed empty. After I was done, I stood listening. She was in there somewhere.

"Miss Brandon," I called.

No answer. I shrugged my shoulders. I always wondered, at this point, what would happen if I just went on about my duties. I had a feeling she would have tackled me before I got outside the door.

"Come here!" I roared. "Damn it!"

Suddenly she was in the doorway, regarding me with fearful eyes. She had her hand up to her trembling mouth. She was wearing a long black dress, severely buttoned all the way from the neck down to her ankles. I gazed at her, standing with hands on hips, my legs braced wide.

"When I call, I want you to come, damn it," I said.

Her voice was trembly. "Please," she said. "Please."

"Please, hell," I said roughly. "You know what I want. Git naked."

"I can't today," she said. "Please, not today. I can't. . . ."

"Shut up," I said. I went close, her flinching away, putting up one hand to ward off my threatening fist. "Don't talk back to me. Ain't I done told you, don't never talk back to me?"

10

She cowered, her fingers frantic on the many buttons, the black fabric parting inch by inch to show her naked breasts. Hands on hips, I stood watching. She was tall, too skinny for my taste, but she had a fine belly on her, and a good leg. Quicker than a fellow would have thought, she showed me all her nakedness, while she stood with head hanging, her eyes closed. Her face was pale and drawn.

With a rough movement I put my hands to her shoulders and pushed at the unbuttoned dress until it fell to her feet. She moaned.

"Down on your knees," I said.

She dropped down, her hands clutching at my legs. Even in her fear, her head pressed warmly against my thighs. "Please, please, please," she was saying. "Don't make me do it. Don't make me, please, please. . . ."

"Take Him out," I said, unheedful of her pleading.

Her hands fumbled at my zipper, she laid both hands on Him, her cheek against Him, saying, "Oh, God, no, you'll give me a baby. Please, God, anything but that."

I stood there until she had got her fill of what was coming to her. Then I said, "Lay down."

There was a shag rug convenient on the tile floor, where a person would stand to use the cutting board. She laid back on it, her knees tight together, her hands clutched over her breasts. I didn't like her eyes as she gazed up at me in stark terror. So I looked at her body instead while I took off my pants and stood over her, letting her see Him full and clear.

Her breath was coming now in ragged gusts. "Just . . . let me . . . just . . . anything . . . just don't give me a baby."

"Open your legs," I said.

Unwilling, the legs opened of themselves, the

11

knees up and swaying apart, offering me the all of her. I got down on my knees and put my hands under her hips, lifting her.

"Why do you have to do this to me?" she said frantically. "I ought to call the police. It's rape, nothing but rape, that's all it is, plain old rape, and—"

"Shut up," I said. "I don't like to hear a woman talking while I fuck her. So just shut up."

I slammed Him into her up to the hilt in the one move, her head going back, her arms flinging out wide as though she was crucified. "Ahhh," she said. "Oh, you're killing me. Ahhhhhh . . ."

I slapped her on one side of the face, saying, "Shut up, damn it, you want the whole neighborhood . . . ?" and that drove her into it, her body threshing under me like she was having a fit. Her mouth was open, screaming soundlessly, and I had all I could do just to stay with her and ride her out to the end.

She had reached it, but she still hadn't put her arms or her legs around me. She lay panting, her head twisting to one side and then to the other like she was dying. Until, watching her eyes, I started stroking her of my own accord; then her head stopped still and she gazed at me, our eyes locked together, and she listened to Him working in her, her body answering to the thrusts in spite of her mind being all against it.

"Don't come in me," she whispered. "Please don't come in me. I won't have your ugly baby in my body, it would be a rape baby, you make me do it, if I didn't do it you'd kill me, wouldn't you, you'd beat me up, please don't come . . ."

I stayed with her, making her believe I was coming in her. I could feel her whole body fighting me, her pussy as cold as ice, so that, like always, it hurt Him. Then, right in the midst of her begging, right when she was sure that this time I was going to

12

give it to her for sure, I pulled Him out and laid Him on her belly so she could see the spurt of it, feel it wet and hot on her naked skin.

I got off of her, like I always did, without delay. She lay with her eyes closed, the lids pale and trembling, while her hand moved on her belly, wet with the come, circling slowly, slowly, wet with her salvation.

I put on my pants, stood over her again. She was still rubbing the stuff into her belly like it was a body lotion, her hand moving, slow but steady, her eyes still closed. There was a peaceful look to her face now, all the hate and anger gone, along with the terrible fear she had of Him. And of me.

"I want some money," I said, making my voice rough.

"My purse is on the counter," she murmured.

I found the big pocketbook, opened it, fumbled through all the junk for her wallet. I took out the wad of bills—she always had two or three hundred dollars—and flipped through them. Taking a one-dollar bill, I put it in my pocket before I dropped the rest of the money fluttering down on her naked body, falling between her legs, sticking to her sticky belly.

"That's all you really want is the money, isn't it?" she said. "First you want to rape me, and then you want to rob me. That's all it is, isn't it?" But her voice was quiet with the words, like talking about the weather, so I didn't have to say anything.

From the doorway, I looked back at her. She was lying curled on her side now, her legs drawn up to her belly, the bills scattered around her on the floor. She was already half-asleep, at peace with herself.

I figured that was it for the day, because the next old lady, I knew, had house guests, and the one after that had been gone for two weeks. I hoped she wouldn't come back, to tell the truth, because she was so weird she made Miss Brandon seem like an ordi-

13

nary everyday sort of woman. Sometimes she even scared me.

But I had forgotten that I had another new one, the next to last on my route, so it was nearly noon before I got to her house.

She might be an old lady, I told myself on first sight of her, but, my goodness, she was something else. A blond, with baby-blue eyes, a leg short but shapely, a body so soft and luscious it just wouldn't quit. And straight out about it, too.

She was waiting for me. I could tell it the minute I walked in the door, carrying the one small sack of groceries.

"Well, hello," she said, her eyes sparkling with mischief. "My friend Sally just called, said I ought to be sure and order my groceries from Adams' Grocery. Now I know why."

"Good morning," I said abashedly, moving to put the groceries on the kitchen counter.

"Sally was so *mysterious* about it," she said, moving close with a snaky movement of her whole body. "But I guessed, knowing Sally . . ." She laughed suddenly. "How was she, grocery boy. Good stuff?"

"I don't . . . I don't know what you're talking about," I said.

She put her hand boldly onto my crotch. "Come on, now, don't act so innocent with *me*." She cocked her head, smiling up into my face. "I know all about you fellows that make home deliveries. You see more ass than you can shake a stick at, don't you?"

"Ma'am," I said with dignity, drawing away, "I wish you wouldn't . . ."

"Oh, I'm not going to rape you, like Sally probably did," she said, chuckling wholeheartedly. "Couldn't do it today if I wanted to, anyway, because I've got my period. I just want to find out what Sally was so damned smug about." Her hand was inside

14

my pants by now, groping for Him. Her breath caught. "Oh, my, yes," she said. She put one arm around my waist, holding me still. "And you're just a growing boy."

"Ma'am," I said, "I wish you wouldn't . . ."

"I wish I *could*," she said, a gay lilt in her voice. She had Him out now, her warm hand stroking, so that for the first time this morning I felt it myself. Maybe it was because I knew she couldn't; anyway, I put my arm around her waist and pulled her close and with all of my own free will I put my mouth on hers, pulling her up on tiptoe as I did it, she was so tiny and so warm.

"Oh, yes," she said softly. "It's going to be a nice, hot summer, isn't it? Except . . ." She laughed softly. "You must promise to make my delivery before Sally's."

"I promise," I said.

Suddenly she disappeared from my arms, sinking down, her arms going around both my legs as her mouth swallowed Him, taking Him deep, her lips sliding warm and lovely, bringing the stuff so quick it surprised me. She didn't flinch, but took it all, so that I felt my legs beginning to quiver, and all I could think about was that I was glad Mr. William had his friend down from New York and so wouldn't be interested this week.

She stood up. Her mouth was soft and bruised, her eyes were glowing. "You're quite a fellow," she said. "But I suppose you know that."

"I just deliver groceries," I mumbled, dropping my eyes so I wouldn't have to look at her.

Her busy little hand tucked Him away, zipped up my fly, and with a loving pat withdrew. She then patted her hair back into place, smiling in fond memory of Him.

"How much did Sally give you?" she asked.

15

"Five dollars," I said.

She laughed, a silvery tone in the still kitchen. "Don't you think you owe *me* this time?"

"Yes'm," I said. "I reckon so." And taking out my billfold, I gave her the five dollars.

She looked at it, and for just an instant a dark expression flowed across her face. Her mouth drooped, and all the gayness had gone out of her so completely that for a minute I thought I had made a mistake. But darn it, I told myself, a fellow can't know all the ins and outs of what they want, no matter how hard he may try. How can he, when so much of the time they don't even know themselves . . . or, at least, won't let themselves know that they know it?

But it was only for an instant; then the gayness of her spirit came back into her. With a quick movement she tore the bill in two and handed me half of it.

"Next time you come, you'll get the rest," she said. "All right?"

"All right," I said. "I reckon."

Her little hand came up to pat my cheek. "Oh, you're something else, you know that?" she said. Her words quickened. "And next time, I'll show you something. I'll make you know Sally is nothing but an old stick-in-the-mud. So you just go on about your business." She laughed softly. "That is, if you've got any business left to transact today. . . . And I'll see you next week. All right?"

"All right," I said bashfully.

Now, that was just one morning delivery out of the many, all that long summertime when the visitors were on their vacations, living in their old and new houses all along the beach road. Of course, there were differences. There were those who only wanted to talk about it, flirt with the idea, with absolutely no intention of doing anything drastic. They could come close to fooling you with it, too, into thinking they

16

really wanted Him. Some there were who never gave me a second glance; I was nothing in the world but just another delivery boy as far as they were concerned. Some wanted it once, but then acted like it hadn't ever happened, no sir, not in a million years had they opened their legs to a delivery boy, no sir, not a fine lady like them.

I took them as they came. I smiled and talked and laughed, or I came and went as silent as the tomb, and maybe I had made their day brighter because I had come and gone, and maybe I hadn't. But I tried.

So you see, I ain't no stud. Ain't *never* been no stud. It's just that I can't help but know how it is with these old ladies. I can't help feeling sorry for their lonesomeness; if they need me to smile, or growl at them, or maybe even, once in a while, strike them with my hand . . . well, who am I to say them nay? There is such great emptiness in the life of a woman alone, all the losses and heartbreaks that I never knew the details of—or hardly ever—but that I could feel in them, because a lady has got to feel something deep and needful to cast a lustful eye on a sixteen-year-old delivery boy . . . eighteen, I mean, because I always told them that when they asked.

So I don't want nothing said against them. I won't hear it, no sir, because my old ladies were each and every one just the finest kind of women, not a bad one or a bitchy one in the lot, not if you understood their doings like I did. I didn't care about the money they gave me, because, not being no stud, I didn't deal with them for the sake of the money. Didn't ever *take* money unless they had to give it out of something needful inside themselves, where the giving of the money would put their doings in such a light as they could live with, without feeling bad.

It's that I *see*. Like Billy, my twin brother, could see the prettiness of a Gulf Coast sunrise, or

17

the way a full moon can make the water like silver. It was his talent to see beauty in this world. It is my talent to see beauty in an old lady, and answer to that beauty in the only way I've got to answer. Because any woman is beautiful, if you can just strike the right chord in them, just like every guitar can make music when it's tuned right. So I was sometimes enabled to let them know their own beautifulness, no matter how much they might have let it get bruised and hurt and maybe even sometimes nearly lost forever. Which, to my mind, don't make a fellow no stud, no way you look at it.

Not even after I got to know the old lady named Charlotte Ainsley, and my entire life changed as a consequence. Or, maybe, only got showed the road that I was meant to take, anyway.

Charlotte Ainsley. . . .

The Girl

I was fourteen years old before ever I found out that It was worth money.

It happened like this. Every day of the school year, rain or shine, I had to walk three miles home. I couldn't exactly take my time, because I knew I had to clean up the house spick *and* span before Papa got home from working in the pulpwood, or else take a beating. He did seem to enjoy whipping on a girl, laying me across his lap to hike up my skirt and let down my pants and then going to it with the bare flat of his hand. Sometimes he got so carried away with himself he couldn't seem to stop, and so I would move sore for a day or two afterward. I don't think he ever brought blood, but he sure knew how to blister a girl's cheeks for her.

The first mile was along the high road that ran from Pass Robin to Mobile, Alabama. Along that stretch, I was with other girls and boys, them all

19

laughing and talking and carrying on the way young folks will do. I did little of the laughing, though, and not much more of the talking, because I was ever serious-minded; most of the time I walked alone ahead of the bunch, or alone a dozen steps behind. I enjoyed it just the same, except when one or another brash boy would range up alongside, smirking and grinning, and I'd have to speak nasty to discourage him. I didn't ever carry boys on my mind, like the other girls seemed to do. The idea of a boy never was a burden to me. Or a joy.

The last two miles, I turned off into a country road that wound off into the pinewood barrens. I liked that part of the journey best of all, because, all to my lonesome, I was able to think my own thoughts.

A paved road, but just barely, full of potholes that never got fixed, and with the underbrush hanging close along the drainage ditches. A body could watch squirrels flitting back and forth, little gray ones and great big fox squirrels that was reddish in coat, and often a coon prowling the ditch bank. More than once I saw deer, too, browsing out from cover; I would stop to look at them, and they would raise their heads to look back, their eyes big, their bodies so still you wouldn't think anything could *be* that still, until suddenly—it was always so sudden it made a body jump, because they didn't seem to have to get ready at all—they would leap into the woods, the flags of their tails flying.

Other families besides me and Papa lived down this lonesome road, in the Five Crossroads community that had just the one little store. The men all cut pulpwood for the paper mill. But I was the only child amongst the Five Crossroads families that went to high school; there was a whole flock of kids in grammar school, but they rode a school bus, and besides, it was a different schoolhouse.

20

Papa, naturally, couldn't see the sense in the idea of a girl getting a higher education when, as he said many and many a time, all she'd ever do was get married and hatch a passel of younguns. Said, "A sixth-grade education, which taught me to read and write and figger, has done me in my lifetime, and your mama, when she was alive, couldn't read or write nothing but her name. She managed to raise you all right, didn't she, without all that book-learning?"

I wouldn't have been so stubborn about high school if he hadn't been so dead set against it, I reckon. Not that I didn't enjoy it; geography was my favorite subject, because I could sit and dream about them faraway places, and what kind of person I might be had I been born and raised there instead of in these pine-barren backwoods, where nobody even tried to farm anymore, and the only work to be had was cutting pulpwood for the paper mill.

I hadn't even been to Pass Robin more than half a dozen times in my life, at which times Mama would give me a quarter for the picture show. Mama had died of the malaria, then, and Papa didn't ever happen to think how much a girl could enjoy a picture show once in a great while. So I hadn't even been to town for some time.

So there I was this particular day, moseying along the road to home, minding my own business and thinking my own thoughts, when I learned the big secret. There was but little traffic on this road, so when I heard the noise of a car coming, I stopped to turn and look. It was the bread truck that made a regular weekly run to the Five Crossroads store. The fellow driving it was standing up, because there wasn't no seat behind the wheel, and the sliding doors was open to keep the inside cool in the heat of the day.

21

As it passed, I raised one hand to wave. Just beyond, the truck come to a sudden stop, and the driver leaned out to ask, "Want a ride?"

"Just waving howdy," I told him.

It wasn't the old fellow who had been driving the bread truck ever since I could remember. I had thought it was him, which is why I had waved in the first place. He hadn't ever stopped, though.

This new fellow laughed. "Well, come on and ride anyway. It's too hot to walk."

I stood there holding my books, thinking about it. Bound to be cool with the doors open that way. On the other hand, I might get to see a deer if I went quiet and took my time. Before I was done considering, though, I found myself walking around in front of the bread truck and climbing up on the other side. So something had already made up my mind for me.

There was a little jump seat, which I climbed up on after putting my books on the floor. As he started off, I hiked up my skirt to feel the breeze on my legs. He was driving considerably slower than when he had come up behind me; I reckon it was because he was looking at me more than he was watching the road.

"How old are you, girl?" he asked.

"Fourteen," I said. "Why?"

His eyes were bright and sharp at the same time, and I saw him wipe his lips with his tongue while he kept on looking at my bare legs. I guess he was dry in the mouth or something.

"Oh, come on, don't lie to me."

"No reason to lie, not that I can see," I told him. "Believe it or not, I'm fourteen, right on."

"Well, you're the prettiest fourteen-year-old girl I've ever seen. I always was a fool for blond hair and blue eyes."

I've always liked my eyes myself; spent many an hour gazing at them in a hand mirror. I hadn't ever seen anybody with eyes so blue as mine, or that exact shade of softness. Maybe it was because I was pretty dark-skinned to flaunt white hair and blue eyes, though it come about naturally enough; I got the olive tone to my skin from my papa, who's a lot darker than me, and I got the blue of my eyes from my mama. Don't know where the white hair—what the fellow called blond—had come from, nor didn't know why it should be anything special, when all it had ever got me was to be called "Cotton Top" when I was little.

I didn't exactly know how to answer to a nice compliment like that. So I just smiled to myself and didn't say anything. I noticed, though, that he was driving slower still, and he had stretched one arm to lay his hand on the seat back close to my shoulder. Just easy like, you know, like he didn't know he was nigh unto touching me.

"Won't this thing go any faster?" I said. "I like to feel the wind on my legs."

He made a short, sharp laugh, sort of nervous-sounding. "Why are you in such a hurry to get home?"

I looked at him. "I ain't in no hurry to get anywhere," I said. "I like it wherever I'm at. So I don't need to be in no hurry. I just want to feel the breeze blowing up my skirt."

I don't know what it was. Maybe it was what I had said, though I didn't mean anything by the spoken words; in actual fact, It was the farthest thing from my mind.

Maybe he only wanted to take it that way. We were just coming into a tunnel of trees, in which there was a turnout where an artesian well bubbled up out of a rusty old iron pipe. It was here that I so often saw the pretty deer, come to drink the water, I guess, though people used the place, too, to eat lunch maybe, because there was Coke bottles and old paper

23

sacks scattered here and there. It was darker under these bigger trees, and sort of damp and cool after the bright sun.

He swung the bread truck into the turnout and stopped. He sat still for a minute, not looking at me. I could see It in his face, though, gathering up in his mind. I just sat there, watching the bubbling water pouring out of the artesian pipe. Ferns grew around the little pool, half mud and half water, that surrounded it; somebody had laid planks out across the mud so people could get a drink of that cold water.

His voice was so jerky I couldn't hardly understand the words. Though they were plain enough.

"How about It?"

I sat there and looked at him. A fine-looking fellow, all right, not like the men who have to work in the pulpwood and wear overalls and get old before their time. Not like Papa. He was tall and slim, and he wore a pair of white coveralls that was just as clean as clean could be. He had his name written in thread above his breast pocket, and over the other pocket was the emblem of the bread company he drove route for. Just as fine a looking fellow as you could hope to meet.

He jerked himself around toward me. His eyes were dodging my eyes, but his hand was true. He laid it right between my legs, bare from where I had hiked up my skirt to enjoy the breeze.

"Listen, you can't lie to me about your age. You know what It's all about. So how about It?"

He hadn't planned to sound mean about it, I knew—he was a nicer fellow than that—but he didn't have control of his voice and so it come out sort of nasty-sounding. I noticed, too, that he was trembling all over; he couldn't help it, he wanted It so bad. He hadn't even had a drink of liquor, either, but was

24

cold stone sober. I knew, because I can smell liquor a mile and a half on a fellow's breath.

His hand was scrabbling between my legs, so I slid forward on the seat to make him free of his need to touch me there. His breath sucked in as he worked his way through the flour-sack drawers and his finger found the warm place he was seeking after.

He put his other arm around my shoulders, holding me close. My cheek rubbed against the clean fabric of his white coveralls as I leaned against him, giggling a little because his hand, like a soft little loving animal, was so busy working and probing, and because I liked this fellow who was so tall and clean and with not a breath of liquor on him.

His voice was strained, but at least it had lost the meanness. "Come on. Let's get in the back of the truck."

It was right then that it come to me. Just out of the blue. It was like something had lit up inside of my head, showing me something I hadn't known before, like when all of a sudden you understand fractions for the first time. It was a simple thing, but so new that I was trembling inside with the discovery.

It was, you see, that he needed It so bad. Menfolk always need It, so they'll do anything, say anything, to get It.

So I just opened my mouth. And I told him.

"You'll have to pay me."

It put a stop to him. Even his hand. He didn't move it away, though, only stood there gazing down into my face, his eyes startled and wide.

Then he did remove his hand; he even took a step away. "Well!" he said in a sharp breath. Then: "Why should I pay for It? You like It as much as I do."

"Because you want It so bad," I said. I smiled at him. "You'll pay me. I know you will. Because you're a nice fellow with money in your pocket."

25

"Don't you want It, too?"

I moved my shoulders. "Don't make no never-mind to me."

He stood there, not saying a word. So I leaned down to pick up my books. Which brought him to taw.

"How much?"

I hadn't thought about it, but I didn't hesitate. "You'll have to give me a quarter, or I won't do It," I said. "A whole quarter."

He laughed then, putting his head back and laughing hard, showing white teeth. "Helll" he said. "Get in the back of the truck."

Putting my books down, I did as I was told, waiting while he unlatched the back doors so we could climb up into the body of the truck. It smelled good, all the fresh bread lined up on shelves on each side of the narrow aisle. I walked down the aisle, the fellow so close behind me he was almost touching. I stopped, and without turning to face him, stepped out of my flour-sack drawers, folding them carefully on an empty shelf.

When I turned, he put his arms around me, holding me close, and I could feel his old Thing hard against my leg. He was shaking again, so I held him around his waist, trying to calm him down. It didn't seem to help, though; he only turned his body sideways so he could put his hand on me again, ruffling up the dress to reach my nakedness. I let him do it, thinking about the quarter more than the feeling of his fingers, wondering how it was that the idea had come to mind so all of a sudden. That's how the best ideas always seem to happen, though, ain't it?

He was panting with the need of It. "Lay down," he said, his arms urging me down.

I looked at the floorbed of the truck. "I don't want to get my dress dirty," I said.

So hungry for It, he was past such considerations.

His arms were pressing me backward, so that I had to struggle to keep my feet. But though I may be no bigger than a minute, I'm pretty strong. So I got away from him.

"I don't aim to lay down on no dirty old floor," I said. "I want you to know that I have to do my own washing of my own clothes."

He drew back, paying attention. "Take it off, then."

I shook my head. "I have to wash myself, too." I shook my head harder, to show him I meant what I said. "You'll have to do It standing up."

"When I'm giving you a whole quarter?" he said. "Not on your life."

"All right," I said, reaching for my drawers. "A quarter ain't worth having to wash my dress all over again. Not to mention ironing it." I never did wear a dress, or anything else, without ironing it so neat and clean and starchy. I was proud of always wearing clothes like that, no matter how much work it entailed.

"Then I'll lay down, and you can get on top," he said hastily.

I looked at him dubiously. "Can It be done that way?"

He put his hands on my breasts, squeezing hard. "It can be done lots of ways," he said happily. "That's one of the best. Don't you know that?"

"I ain't never done It in no such a way," I said. "But all right, I'll try it. I just don't aim to get myself or my dress dirty, that's all."

I had to laugh secretly to myself then, because he didn't have any intention of getting his pretty white coveralls dirty, either. No sir. He proceeded to take them off and lay them up on a shelf, and only then did he take off his shorts and lay down buck naked on the floor.

I stood looking down at him. His old Thing was

as slim as a pencil, so neat and pretty-looking, not a great ugly club of a Thing with black hair all around it. His hair was red, and curled tightly, and the Thing was just as red as fire, and I could see a pulse jumping in it, making it jerk. A nice Thing. And him without a drop of liquor in his head to urge him on, either.

Still and all, I had to make sure of myself. So when he said, full of impatience, "Come on, come on, damn it," I said, "No, sir. I want my quarter first."

See, I already knew that part of it, too, without having to be told by a wiser head. Get your money first, that's what I figured, while he was in the need of It, because after he got his satisfaction, he might not be so ready to shell out the cash. Afterward, it wouldn't seem like nearly so much worth what it cost.

"For God's sake, you little whore, come on, and be quick about it," he said angrily

It was the first time I had ever heard the word, and I didn't know what it meant. Still, from the tone of his voice, it got my back up.

"I ain't no whore," I said. "I just want my money, that's all."

He laughed then, like he couldn't help but laugh. "It's in my coverall pocket," he said. "Get it yourself."

He had a whole pocket full of change. I held it cupped in the palm of one hand while I picked out a shiny new quarter; then I poured it carefully back into the pocket. Holding the quarter tightly in my hand, so I could feel it sharp-edged against my palm, I hiked up my skirt and began tying it around my waist.

He looked at my legs. "Take off your dress," he said. "Aren't you going to let me see you naked?"

I shook my head, kneeling down over his hips, not knowing how to do It but doing It anyway, slipping myself over his old Thing slow and easy and then just resting there, watching his face.

"Nice?" I said.

"Oh, God, yes," he groaned.

I let myself feel his Thing for just a minute, watching his face work. I sort of liked It this way, because there wasn't any big man-weight crushing me down; I was such a tiny girl, a body could feel smothered sometimes, and the heavy liquor breath in my face so I couldn't breathe. This way was so nice I laid out on him, pillowing my head on his chest, and just let my pussy take over and do what it ought to do. What, I must admit even to myself, it *wanted* to do, because it was making money hand over fist.

So I worked on him and he began to breathe heavier and he began to arch, and I kept on working until he was thrashing under me, pounding up at me in the throes of his manhood, and I laughed, I actually laughed, when his old Thing gushed its juice, and kept on gushing, and I could feel how the muscle throbbed in me and kept on throbbing, slower and slower and slower, until he was still at last and I lay quiet on him, his arms holding me, my head snuggled to his nice clean hairless chest, and we were quiet for a minute.

He made to get up finally, but I said, "Wait a minute." So he waited a minute, and I don't know how I knew it would do him good, but I put my mouth on the nipple of his chest and sucked at it like a child will suck, while he put his arms around my head, holding my mouth hard against him whilst I flicked his nipple with my tongue.

So his old Thing grew ready again, and it was nice to know that I could make it hard again, for that's a woman's power over a man, when all is said and done. This time I went so easy, letting him take his time, and it was loving and gentle and kind, and

29

when his old Thing let it go again, it was so nice for him I could read it in his face and in his eyes and the way his arms held me.

After I was sure he had finished, I sat back on my heels whilst he gazed at me, saying over and over again, "Good God, girl. Good God, where did you learn to do It like that?"

I said, "I ain't never done It on top before. It's nice, ain't it?"

He kept on staring at me, lying there naked in the sight of my eyes, like he couldn't believe what he had just felt. Pure wonderment dwelled in his face.

I stood up and got busy shaking out my dress, smoothing the skirt down over my hips and pushing my hair back into place. It was sort of sweaty in the back of the truck, with the doors closed and all.

"You're really only fourteen?" he said at last.

"I told you. Ain't no reason for lying," I said. "I got to go now. Thank you for the quarter."

He got to his feet, so slow about it I knew he didn't want to believe he had already used up his payment.

"But you ... you're not ... you've done It before, I know you weren't ..."

"It wasn't ever as nice as this," I told him sincerely. "Papa always has to get hisself dog-drunk first." I wrinkled my nose. "I hate the smell of liquor. I just hate it."

"Good God!" he said, stopping in putting on his coveralls to stare at me all over again. "You mean to say your own father ..."

"Ever since Mama died," I said. I could read the proudness in my voice. "I've been a woman grown since I was ten years old. Been having my monthlies, and all."

Ready now, I smoothed down my skirt one more time and thanked him again for the nice gift of money. He wanted to put his arms around me, but I wasn't

30

having any of that. I opened the doors myself and climbed out, got my books from the cab, and walked on down the road before he could get dressed enough to follow. I reckon I knew I'd done good, and it was time to quit.

After a while, he slowed the bread truck alongside me, leaning out to speak. "You come this way often?"

"Every schoolday," I told him. "But . . . it'll cost you a quarter every time."

He nodded, and laughed, and then his face got serious. "You mustn't tell anybody, since you're so young. If you tell, it'll get me in trouble sure enough."

"Why would I be talking?" I said. "It's my own business, ain't it?"

So he went his way, and I went mine, and I was so proud that I had found out the great thing about being born a woman. Fourteen years old, and already knew the secret that a lot of womenfolk never learn their life long—that men, when they need It, will give just about anything to get It. So these silly women, they go along and go along giving it away, and feel downright proud of such doings. Well, I want to tell you, I was so proud of *my* doings, I just skipped along home, the quarter clutched in my hand, and when I got there I forgot entirely to clean up the house, I was so busy marveling over that piece of money I had earned so easily. It was the first money I had ever made in my life.

My mama always said that it looked like every time something nice happens to a person, something bad has to come along to balance it off. That's been more or less my own experience of life, too; but it don't mean that you've got to act the blame fool and bring it on yourself. But it was my own fault that, when Papa got home from the pulpwood, I was still sitting there admiring my brand-new shining quarter, and not a bed made or a floor swept.

31

The minute I heard his step on the front porch, I flew up and started in; but of course it was too late. He stood in the doorway before I had hit a dozen licks with the broom, glaring at me; it hadn't taken but one glance to show him that I had done wrong.

"I don't know what I'm going to do about you," he said in his heavy voice. "Here I done raised me the prettiest little girl that ever laid foot to the ground, and I can't persuade you to do a lick of work of your own free will."

I looked at him, already trembling inside, because that was the way he always talked when he'd taken a drink or two coming home from work.

My papa was a big man, broad of shoulder and thick of leg, hulking in his overalls twice the size of an ordinary fellow. He was dark-complected and he didn't shave but about once a week, on a Friday night, when he got paid for all the pulpwood he had cut. It was always his brag that he could cut twice as much pulpwood and drink three times as much whiskey as the next fellow; I don't know about the cutting, but I believed him about the drink, all right, because I had seen him do it.

"Papa, I got kept after school," I said. "I'll have the house redded up long before it's time to put supper on."

He came on into the room and stood towering over me. I reached not much higher than his belt buckle, because I was ever a tiny thing, and a woman to boot. And my excuse only made things worse.

"Kept after school?" he said, his voice thudding at me like his hand would be doing before next Tuesday. "I guess you've been back-sassing your teachers." He shook his head, wagging it slowly in pious wonderment. "I just don't know how I could get me such a pretty little thing, and have her grow up so ornery and mean," he said. "Doggone it, girl, I ain't never seen the match to you, with them blue eyes and that white hair

32

and just built no bigger than a minute. So why is it that you can't do as good as you look?"

"I try, Papa," I cried out. "I try to be good." I was shaking inside like that fellow had been shaking, holding me so close with his hand between my legs. But not for the same reason; I was fearful of the beating, not desiring it.

"I'm just going to have to teach you again, I reckon," he said slowly. "I purely hate to raise my hand to a pretty thing like you, but, by God and by damn, I aim to raise you right if it kills me." He stopped suddenly. "You ain't lying to me about being kept in after school? You ain't been walking the woods with one of them highfalutin high-school boys?"

That really scared me, because he hadn't ever spoke any such suspicion before.

"You know I don't like them old boys!" I yelled at him. "You know I won't have nothing to do with them, even when they try to walk with me, and carry my books, and all. I don't give 'em the time of day, Papa. You know I wouldn't give them the time of day."

"I'd better not hear of it, or you won't sit down for a week," he said. "You're a woman grown, you know, been having your monthlies since you was ten years old. Open your legs to one of them horny boys, you'll be bringing me home a bastard to shame me in front of the neighbors."

"I wouldn't do no such a thing!" I cried out. "I don't even *like* them old boys!"

He wiped his broad hand across his big face. "Good God, the burdens of a father with a motherless girl to raise," he said. "Knowing there ain't a man in creation that could look at you without wanting to do It to you. No man worth his salt, anyway."

I began to get a hope that this sidetrack to his mind might save me. But as I watched him walk across the room to where he kept his jug of whiskey, my

33

heart sank. It was going to be a bad one this time, after all.

He lifted the jug of piney-woods rotgut and taken a hearty swig. He wiped his mouth with the back of his hand and took another sample, smaller this time, just for the taste. Though how he could stand that old taste of whiskey, I don't know. I never could bear the smell of it, myself.

Putting the jug on the table, he turned to study me for a long minute. Then he walked to a straight chair and sat down.

"Come here," he said.

"Papa," I said, begging him.

"Come here, I said."

I knew it wasn't no use. I could feel the numbness in the muscles of my legs as I moved to stand beside him. Even sitting in the chair, his face was on a level with mine, so that I couldn't help seeing into his eyes. The spark showed, all right, glowing deep and yellow, the way the eyes of an animal will glow. He had a real beast in him, I knew well, that he couldn't always keep on a leash, and this time, maybe because of the quarter still clutched in my hand to hide it from him—if he saw it, he'd sure God want to know where it had come from—I knew for sure he'd let loose all holts.

His big hand fitted firmly into the small of my back, pushing me down across his legs. I gritted my teeth, waiting while he lapped my dress up into the small of my back and pushed down my pants to bare the flesh. He laid his hand on my ass, so big it just covered me all, and rubbed it, circling, like he was petting me instead of punishing.

"God knows I hate to have to whip you like this," he said. "But I got to raise you right."

I knew it would only make it worse if I said anything.

His hand lifted and hung, hovering. "Ain't that right?"

34

"Yes, Papa," I said, and then cried out sharply as the big hand came down so hard it must have raised a welt.

I had tried once to outlast him by not crying or whimpering; but it had drove him so crazy that he nigh beat me to death. He wanted to hear my repentence loud and clear, so when he hit me the second time, I didn't try to hold back, but squalled like a cat.

The hand started patting me again, moving up and down, his fingers trailing in the crack, and while he did it he kept on exhorting me, talking about what a beautiful woman I was growing to be, and how I had to be lovely in soul as in body, and then he hit me again. I started crying helplessly, gulping the strain out of my throat, and my flesh was aching from the last blow and from waiting for the next, and under me I could feel his Thing rising to a stand, like it always did when he beat on me in such manner. I used to wonder why whipping me took him that way, when he hated so to do it; but it was such a natural part of the punishment by now that I didn't even wonder about it anymore. I hadn't ever seen his Thing, only felt it under me in his overall breeches whilst he was beating the sinfulness out of me.

It was rough this time, all right. He just kept on and kept on until I felt like I couldn't stand it another minute. I lay just limp with anguish, my head hanging down, and I was so sore the petting hurt nearly as much as the whipping. I knew I wouldn't hardly be able to walk tomorrow morning.

But there happened inside of me a funny thing, this particular time. I still had my quarter in my hand, you see, and even while he was working on my salvation so hard it was killing me, I kept my mind fixed on what I had learned today. It was a bright and shining thing in my head, just as new and pretty as my first earned quarter itself, and so somehow the whipping didn't tear me up like it had always done before,

35

but sort of like it was happening to somebody else instead of me.

When he was through at last, I stood up, my skirt falling to cover up my shame, as he called it, and looking into his face, I didn't flinch from seeing what I saw.

"You think you can do better now?" he demanded.

"Yes, Papa," I said.

He heaved a sigh. "It's the only way I know how to do with a girl like you," he said heavily. "Lord knows I hate to put a hand to your pretty body in such anger. Now, kiss me, and get about your work."

He always wanted me to give him a kiss of forgiveness, so I put my arms around his shoulders and laid my mouth on his mouth, tasting the whiskey and smelling it, too, so that I had to hold my breath. His big arms, coming around me, held me close before he shoved me away.

"Now, get about it," he growled, and went to take another drink as a reward for his labors.

As I went about the housework and the cooking of supper, I took the chance of washing out a Mason fruit jar and drying it carefully and lining it with Reynolds wrap, so nobody could see what might be inside. I took it into my bedroom and dropped the quarter into the jar. It rang against the empty bottom. For as much as a minute I stood gazing down on its lonesomeness, thinking how heavy the fruit jar would be once I had it filled with quarters.

I meant to fill it. Yes, sir. Now that I had got hold of the secret, I didn't aim to let it get rusty for lack of use. I put the fruit jar up on a whatnot shelf in the corner of my room, crowded otherwise with conch shells and carnival prizes.

I was deathly afraid it wasn't over for the night yet, but the other would have to happen, too, because Papa kept on pulling at his jug of rotgut while I cooked supper, sitting out in the cool of the porch at an angle where he could see me as I worked back and forth across the kitchen. It sure looked like it was shaping up toward one of those long nights, all right, and I hated the very idea, even while knowing there wasn't anything I could do about it.

I found myself wishing that Papa would get married again. He had got married once, a good while after Mama had died. She was a nice lady, too, who I had known all my life and would have been proud to call Mother if she had wanted me to. But she didn't last but for the second of one of Papa's big drunks. She gave him the chance, all right, endured the first one, in which he used her unmercifully, even beating on her the way he beat on me, one time even chasing her out of the bedroom and throwing her down on the floor and taking her right before my eyes. It was just lucky he caught her before she got to the high road, or there might have been a scandal. But she told him the once was enough, and when it happened again she calmly packed up the things she had brought to the household and went home, and we never did see her again.

We ate supper together, silent like always on a night like tonight, and I went to bed early, laying there sore of body in the darkness, waiting to see what would happen. I listened to him out there on the porch in his own separate darkness, not knowing if he had quit the drinking after supper. He always talked to himself, drunk *or* sober.

After the longest while, though, I heard him go to his own bed, take off his overalls and shirt, and lie down with a tired grunt. I knew then that it was all right. I wouldn't have to endure him coming to me in the dark, fumbling naked for the bed to lay his body on top of me, so big and heavy I was just smothered under him, to where I couldn't breathe, his big old Thing pounding at me until I'd be as sore in front as I was behind. And all the time his breath, the very pores of his body, reeking with the liquor, so that I choked every time I had to take a breath, and there wasn't nothing in the whole world but the stink of his breath and the weight of his flesh, and his great Thing thrusting up into me like the blind beast it was, seeking to raven and to destroy.

It wasn't that that I hated the most, though his old Thing must have been something mighty to poke into womankind—I never had seen it, he always came in the dark and left in the dark—because it was blunt and thick and almost scalding in my tender flesh. It was afterward I hated so much, when he cried so pitifully it sounded like he was dying, beating at his crotch with his own heavy fist while he cussed the evil that was in him.

No matter how I tried to soothe him, petting him with my hand and telling him what a good papa he was, it only seemed to make it worse, until he finally passed into the whiskey sleep, still laying heavy and smothering, so huge on my tiny body; and when I woke up the next morning, he would be gone, not just from my bed but all the way out of the house, gone without breakfast to his day of hard work because he couldn't face me in broad open daylight after using me so in the dark.

But it hadn't happened, not tonight, and I was glad clear through, because I had made up my mind. From now on, any man that got to put his old Thing into my sweet pussy would have to pay hard cash for the privilege, if I had my way about it.

Which I meant to do.

The Boy

Charlotte Ainsley didn't belong to the Gulf Coast
like my other old ladies; actually, she said herself
she had borrowed the cottage for the summer from a
dear friend. Not only that, she was English, a cool sort
of woman who spoke the language like it hurt her
mouth to move it. I ain't going to try to imitate the
way she talked, because I can't, but she clipped her
words off like a knife cutting cheese, so that she
sounded impolite even when she didn't mean to be.
When she did want to be impolite, her tone of voice
could chill a body to the bone.

She was older, too, than most of my ladies . . .
must have been close to forty. Wasn't a big woman,
either, though somehow or another you always had a
feeling that she *was* big. She had sharp eyes, with a
glitter of interest in everything about her, and a color
that was somewhere between blue and green, de-

pending on the light. There was a yellow in her eyes, too, so that they looked like the eyes of a cat.

She had a beautiful nose, though you wouldn't have thought so if you had thought about it, because there was a curve to the bridge, with the flanges cut very sharp and fine. Not a large nose, but a definite nose, and her face wouldn't have been the same without it. Because her mouth was too soft and promising, you see, a real woman's mouth.

When she met me in the kitchen the first morning I delivered an order of groceries, she was wearing a pair of white shorts, and her legs, not long but well-shaped, were so tanned it made the shorts look all that much whiter. She was wearing a man's shirt, the tails tied in a knot at her small waist, and it was unbuttoned, showing her belly was tanned, too. The minute I looked, I knew she wasn't wearing anything to support her nice breasts, and I thought to myself, Oh, Lord, here's another one. Little did I know!

"What me to put the groceries up, ma'am?" I asked, like always—though this time it was only one sack, a loaf of bread and a quart of milk and a box of crackers—and she said, "Oh, leave it there on the table. I didn't need the groceries anyway, I just wanted to get a look at you. I'm Charlotte Ainsley."

So I stood there and let her have her look. Which she did; and then she nodded. "Yes. When that girl described you in the powder room at the Yacht Club last night, I thought you might do."

"What girl?" I said, sort of surprised.

She grinned. "The woman who gave you that nice wristwatch you're wearing," she said, and then she laughed. "Are there so many of them?"

I looked at my wristwatch. It was a Rolex, and I liked it a lot. But it made me uneasy that Miss Sarah had been talking about me to the ladies at the Yacht Club, because every time that happened, I got a couple of new customers, and it was already all I could do to keep up with the old ones. It seemed like there just wasn't no way to keep my old ladies from dropping a hint or a brag to another old lady.

So I sighed, inside where she couldn't see it, and said, "It was mighty nice of Miss Sarah to give me such a pretty watch. She's a nice lady, all right."

Miss Charlotte was already through with that subject; in her clipped voice she said, "Come along, then," and turned to walk out of the kitchen without waiting to see whether or not I was following.

Which was a surprise to me, because I didn't hardly ever get invited into the other parts of the house. It was like when it happened in the kitchen it didn't count, like it would have counted in the bedroom.

I left the sack of groceries on the kitchen table and followed Miss Charlotte. The living room was all wicker furniture, old and comfortable, the room darkened and cooled against the Gulf Coast sun by heavy drapes over the windows. We didn't stop there, but went out onto a sun porch that faced not toward the Gulf but away from it.

She had made it into a workroom, rolling up the fiber rug against the house wall and laying down a canvas sheet like a house painter would use, and all the wicker furniture was shoved back out of the way, leaving a clear space in the middle. In that space there was a stand with some kind of artistic work on it, modeled out of clay, and around about was all the paraphernalia she needed to make such things.

"Look at him," she said, so I looked at the piece she was working on. It was something else, I can tell you, shaped strong and right, and I thought to myself that Billy sure would have liked to see it, unfinished though it was. It was the sort of thing, like a Gulf Coast sunrise or a flight of pelicans, that it pleased him to look at when he was alive.

I went close and walked around it. There wasn't
41

anything there that said "Male," because you couldn't say this was an arm and that was a leg and here was the shape of a thigh. It was all molded too much together, you see, for your eye to break it down into parts. But somehow or other she had made it to say "Male!" right on, in the strength and flow of the lines, in the mass of the unfinished clay.

"What do you think?" Miss Charlotte said.

"It's . . . it's nice," I said.

"Nice?" she said dryly. "It's *great,* young man, the best piece I've ever done." She frowned. "Only if . . . there's something missing. There must be one absolutely naturalistic observation, the central fact of a man, the . . ."

I wasn't listening, because I didn't know what she was talking about, and couldn't have understood it if I had known. Instead I was studying her hands, thinking that they had done this job of work. Not big hands, but strong, the fingers short and shapely, and I thought there would be a roughness in the skin; they're useful, not just a woman's hands; they would have to earn a roughness to do the work she calls on them to do.

She quit talking—to herself as much as to me, I knew, because I wasn't paying any attention to her words. Then she said, turning around, "So let me have a look at you."

"What?" I said.

"Take it out so I can see it," she said impatiently. "Your cock, old cock."

I felt myself drawing back. "It's not an it, it's Him," I said.

She turned her head to one side, peering at me with her bright eyes like a bird. Her voice softened. "All right, Him, then."

"Ma'am," I said.

"Oh, come along, don't be bashful," she said.

42

"Every woman without her own man along the Gulf Coast has seen Him and used Him. You're notorious, my dear fellow. So don't come the bashful-boy bit with me."

I stood just frozen, wishing these old ladies would learn to keep their mouths shut. It seemed like every time one of them got the use of Him, she had to whisper about it to her friends. Looks like they'd want to keep the secret to themselves, don't it? But I guess they couldn't help bragging about Him. For which I can't truly blame them, I reckon.

When I didn't move, Miss Charlotte came close, her strong fingers suddenly at the belt buckle of my khaki pants and then pushing them down on my hips. Nothing else for it, so I stepped out of my jockey shorts of my own free will.

"My, my, that *is* a nice one," Miss Charlotte said. "No wonder your ladies are as proud as peacocks."

Stooping, she took Him in hand to observe closely as she skinned the head bare, then shaped her hand underneath Him. He lay limply in her palm.

"I need Him standing," she said, and closing her fist, began to pump gently. I had been right; there *was* a roughness to her palm that felt so nice, the way she was using her hand, and of course He got up and stood just like she wanted Him to.

Taking her hand away, she stepped back, then to one side to take Him in profile. He stood up at a sharp angle, jerking slightly.

She nodded thoughtfully. "Yes. That's what I need. One utterly naturalistic object, embedded in the very heart and center of the piece. It'll be shocking, it'll ram the message and the meaning home like nothing else." She lifted her head. "I want you to pose for me. Will you do it?"

"Ma'am?" I said.

"I want you to model your cock for my manhood

43

sculpture," she said in that quick impatience. "First I'll do an entirely separate model of Him, I'll have to get to know Him utterly, you understand, and I can't risk ruining my statue. When I'm satisfied, I'll add Him to the sculpture."

"Ma'am, I've got groceries to deliver," I said.

"Groceries? They're not important." She shrugged. "Even servicing your old ladies isn't important, alongside this, though I'm sure it's quite profitable for you." She gazed at me, her eyes bright. "Don't you realize that I shall make Him immortal? Long after you're an old man, and He's a shriveled bit of rawhide that's worth only pissing through, He'll be standing proud and young in a great museum somewhere, with people pausing every day to gaze upon Him, and know a real cock for once in their lives." She was regarding me shrewdly. "Think of the women who, seeing Him so, will yearn so fervently to possess Him they'll simply be burning with lust. Immortality, my dear boy, is not to be sneered at, however it may come."

She had something there. I had to admit it. Something to think about. I wondered what Billy would have said to such a proposition, had he lived to get his growth. Billy was dead and gone now, like one of these days I would be also, and not a mark to show my passing through this world except in the fond memory of an old lady here and there—if any were left by then to remember at all. Just like Billy had failed to leave his mark, from dying so young, except in the memory of *my* mind.

She was circling around her work now, studying it while she talked at me. "You see, boy, I'm not like your other friends. Sure, I want to use you. But not like they're using you. To them you're only a nice young stud whom they can fuck with guilt or love, obligated only to the payment of money or a beautiful watch. You're a dream come true, a dream that every

44

woman, I suppose, carries somewhere in the back of her mind, a really great cock without the emotional involvement of a man attached to it. Men are always thinking of women that way, making them bed pieces pure and simple. It would shock most men to know that women can entertain the same silly, unrealizable dream. Except that you do, miraculously, realize it for them, and that's why they have to tell one another all about it. Only by telling someone else can they prove to themselves they've had you, bought and paid for in every way except with their hearts, which is the only way most women—unlike men—can purchase the fulfillment they need."

"You mean you just want me to stand here while you shape Him up in the clay?" I said.

She stopped pacing. But she didn't stop talking. "So they use Him. But they use Him up, they drain Him. I'll use Him too, my dear, of course I will. The artist is ruthless, you know, absolutely without pity where the work is concerned. But I won't use Him up at all, I'll make Him greater, the absolute quintessence of malehood. Your cock will become the immortal archetype of all malehood, the classic cock of enduring time. All men will be measured against the great ideal I shall shape with my talent and my two hands."

"How long will it take?" I said. "I got groceries to deliver."

"It shall not be abstract sculpture, you understand, not this part. It shall be done in infinite detail, every vein engorged with blood, the knob glowing in lust, the balls knotted to cast out strongly the sperm of your being. I must come to know every vein, every sinew, sense the lining of the tube, measure to the thousandth of an ounce the weight and heft of your balls. . . ."

Near me again, she put both hands on Him this

45

time, feeling Him, measuring Him, knowing Him like no woman had known Him yet.

"I'll quit my job," I said.

"Yes," she said, looking up into my face. "There's nothing more important. You see that, don't you? You understand now."

"Yes'm," I said. "I'll tell Mr. Adams I have to take off a few days. I'll come when you want me to come, I'll stay as long as I have to."

"A few days!" she cried. "It'll take weeks. Maybe months." She was still holding Him, gripping Him so hard it almost hurt. But it felt good, too, because her hands were knowing Him. They were hands meant to know Him, tough and skillful in the knowing. I felt as carried away as she was.

"All right. Weeks, then. Months." She had roused me, so I reached for her.

"Now, wait a minute!" she said sharply, pulling away. "There'll be none of that."

I guess I showed stupidness when she kept me from touching her. I'm not generally stupid around an old lady, but then, I had never met an old lady like unto her. She certainly had seemed stirred up to the point of needfulness, which was why I had tried to put my hands on her, desiring to give, to the best of my ability, what she surely wanted.

"You mean you don't want to ... ?"

She laughed. She laughed a long time. "My dear. I'm a lesbian."

"What's that?"

Her face showed disbelief. "You mean you don't know?"

"Never heard the word. You're a woman, ain't you? I ain't never seen a woman who could look on Him and not want ..."

"Yes, I'm a woman, child. A woman who loves other women. I haven't had a man in years."

46

"How can a woman make love to a woman?" I inquired curiously.

Her lips quirked. "You'd be surprised." She patted my arm, moving safely away after having touched me again. "Oh, there was a time for men in my life. For a few years, when I was very young and stupid, a different man for every night, an incredible variety of males, until I came to the point of hating men. I learned, finally, that no man could give me what I was seeking. Then I found it . . . in a lovely woman. I haven't needed men, and their transparent egos, since."

"But you're here all alone. You . . ."

Her mouth softened. "My friend will be along soon. She couldn't get away just yet. Oh, yes, my lovely friend."

"Then you just want me to pose for the statue?"

Her voice briskened. "That's all, my dear. I shall pay you, never fear. What do your ladies give you for your . . . attentions?"

"Oh, they don't pay me," I assured her earnestly.

"What about the wristwatch?"

"That was . . . just a gift. Oh, they hand me a dollar, now and again, for delivering the groceries. But . . ."

She made a sharp laugh. "You are an innocent, aren't you? With your talents, you could be driving a Cadillac and wearing the finest clothes. Why, I know some ladies in London who'd . . ." She paused. "What does the grocery store pay you, then?"

"A dollar an hour."

"That's not even minimum wage."

"Yes'm. Mr. Adams, though, he says he can't afford to pay minimum wage, and besides, he says I'm bound to pick up tips here and there. . . ."

She nodded in that brisk way of hers. "All right. I'll pay two dollars an hour." She grinned. "For as long as you can keep Him up. It must be a standing pose, you understand, no limp fig leaves for us. How long do you think you can keep Him at a stand?"

"I don't know," I said. "I never tried."

"Well, we shall see." She gripped my wrist, looked at my fine new watch. "You'd better get on with your deliveries. Can you tell your boss you're quitting, and be here early in the morning?"

"Yes, ma'am," I said. "Anytime you say."

I started for the doorway into the living room. Her voice stopped me. "Your ladies shall be rather irate, I'm afraid, when they discover you won't be delivering their groceries and hauling their ashes anymore, my dear. How will you manage about that?"

"I don't know," I said. "I ain't thought about it."

"As far as I'm concerned, you can see as many of them as often as you want to." She chuckled. "I have no desire to interfere with your nice hobby. Except . . ." She paused. "You must remember that the important thing is our work together."

"Yes'm, I won't forget," I assured her.

"So avoid going to one of them before you come to me. Afterward, only. We must have the very best of Him, you understand."

"Yes, ma'am, I understand," I said. "You'll have the best. I promise."

She gave me a lovely smile. "You're a charming boy," she said. "And the greatest charm of it all is, you don't even know it."

I had a sudden idea of telling her about Billy, how the idea of him in my head made me the way I was. I always thought about how Billy would have been with people, kind to their needs and all. But she was walking around her piece of work again, her mind gone away into it, away from me, so she didn't need to know what I wanted to tell her. So I went on.

It did upset people something terrible when I quit delivering groceries for Old Man Adams. This skinny, red-headed kid took my place; but Mr. Adams called me the first day, all upset about the flood of complaints, and would I come back to keep his customers happy? Said he'd raise me to two dollars an hour. But by then I had already been back to Miss Charlotte's house for the first day of posing, so he couldn't change my mind. I did the best I could—I took the route one day with the other boy, to sort of introduce him, and whilst doing so I let my old ladies know that even if I wasn't delivering groceries anymore, I would be handy for any odd jobs that might come up, like cutting grass or heavy cleaning. All they had to do was call me on the phone and I'd make time for their needs. So that turned out all right, and I could put my mind on the business with Miss Charlotte.

She wanted me bright and early each morning before I got caught into something else, which meant before sunrise. That was all right with me, because I do like to be out and doing at such a time of day. I could walk along the beach from my house to her house—I lived out on a point, because my daddy called himself a commercial fisherman in case he ever took the notion to work again, and though the point was a valuable piece of waterfront land now, my family had lived there since anybody could remember, in a big old frame house that hadn't been painted in so long it was weathered gray. It stood on stilts so the high water could wash under it, and because there was so much salt in the ground, there wasn't but just a few tough bunches of grass here and there in the yard.

It was a sort of pleasant thing to go scuffling along the beach every morning, to knock at Miss Charlotte's front door—no more going in through the kitchen for me—to have her greet me cheerily, ready to go to work.

That first morning—every morning thereafter, as a matter of fact—we shared a pot of coffee and a nice

49

conversation. Miss Charlotte wanted to know all about me, when I was born and how I was raised and what my daddy was like, and my mama. Asked things I was embarrassed to talk about, too, like did I really take joy in making it with my old ladies, and why didn't I have a girl of my own age to be in love with. When I couldn't answer, I just kept silence until she went on to something else.

Then, briskly looking at her watch, she'd say, "We've got the light now, we must get to work." The screened porch looked out to the north, which, she told me, was just the best light in the world for her kind of work.

I'd take off all my clothes—after the first time, knowing her interest was purely artistic, it wasn't an embarrassment to show myself naked to her gaze— and then she'd do what was necessary to make Him stand. She was terribly interested in the process; the first morning, she even had a great big magnifying glass for closer observation, while her palm with its nice roughness roused Him. Then she sat and studied Him through the magnifier for the longest time, while I stood gazing out over the top of her head. In fact, that first day she didn't do anything *but* look, every time he began to lose interest bringing Him up to taw all over again.

The next thing, she started in to sketching him in charcoal on sheet after sheet of a great pad of drawing paper. She sat close to Him, working very quickly from one angle or another, whilst He was at His peak. But every single sketch dissatisfied her, it seemed like; while I took a rest, she would study the latest one with a scowling distaste before throwing it into the wastebasket and starting all over again.

We quickly came to realize there was going to be a problem with keeping Him at his best for as long a period of time as she wanted to work every day. I did

50

my part the best I could, thinking the thoughts and running through the pictures in my mind that would make Him rise up eager for business. I could manage fifteen minutes at a time, maybe even as much as half an hour; but then, in spite of myself, he would start to wilt.

She was mighty impatient; she seemed to think that a fellow ought to be able to keep a hard-on just as long as she needed it. Just any old hard-on wouldn't do her, either—it had to be the fullest and the strongest, just this side of losing it, all gorged and red and with a painful thump. After an hour or two of such strain, I'd get the stone ache so bad I couldn't hardly stand straight.

She didn't understand why that should be, either. But it interested her. Over and over again I had to describe just how it got started, a tiny ache down there under the balls—I put her finger right on the place— and then grow and grow until you felt like the pit of your stomach was going to drop out.

I must say, Miss Charlotte did her part, too. No matter how impatient she got, when she had to use her hand to fetch Him up to taw she did it gently and thoughtfully, and whilst she was sketching she'd talk bawdy, keeping my interest up, and once in a while she'd reach over and stroke Him with just one finger, smiling to see Him jerk and throb.

Come the third day, though, we had found real trouble. Ever an independent cuss, He had a mind of his own, you understand, and He just decided He couldn't see anything good for Himself in all this foolishness. So He just decided He wouldn't come to a stand today at all, and no matter how she coaxed and played, He stayed stubbornly limp.

She said angrily, "You've been wasting Him with those women."

"No, ma'am," I protested. "I'm supposed to mow

51

some grass for Miss Sally after I get done here today. But I ain't seen nobody since we started."

"Have you been masturbating?"

"What's that?"

She told me, and I said, "No, ma'am, I never was much of a one to go in for that sort of thing."

She smiled, sort of, and said, "Then how did you find out when you were a man?"

"I was doing this old lady," I said soberly. "It liked to scared me to death, because it was the first time it had happened."

"You mean you were being kind to your ladies even before you could . . . ?"

"Yes'm," I assured her. "They didn't mind at all, because it didn't come to a halt so quick, you see. But that time . . ." I thought about it, remembering. "Just all of a sudden there was this explosion all down my backbone, and I didn't know what was happening, and so I reckon I went sort of crazy there, because I thought I had ruined myself for sure."

With that remembering, he had started to take an interest in life at last, and seeing it, she started to sketching. But He didn't hold it for more than five or ten minutes before starting to draw in on Himself.

"Looks like we're just going to have to wait," I said apologetically. "I'm doing the best I can."

She shook her head. "We can't afford to waste a day's worth of time. Wait a minute."

Going into the house, she came back with a great book. She set it up comfortable on a tall stand so I wouldn't have to hold the weight of it, slanted so I could scan the pages easily enough.

"Now, look at those pictures," she said. "We can talk about them, too, if you wish."

It was all right. The book was just full of these dirty pictures, all in living color, of people doing things to one another that I hadn't ever even thought of. At Miss Charlotte's suggestion, I didn't flip through fast, but lingered over every detail, imagining what it would be like to do it in such manner.

It was educational, right enough, because when I didn't understand what was going on, Miss Charlotte explained it all most carefully. Among other things, I found out, after all, how women can do it to one another; not to mention the things that men do together, and how groups of both men and women and boys and girls can enjoy themselves in strange fashions. But I still couldn't believe—and I told Miss Charlotte so, too—in some of those postures as depicted in that book. In fact, I told her, you'd have to be as limber as a snake to fuck like that. Which made her laugh.

The dirty book got us through the day, but that afternoon Miss Sally got a terrible surprise, because I didn't last but about half a minute. It made her mad, too, but I couldn't tell her the reason for it; Miss Charlotte had sworn me to secrecy about our artistic project.

But looking at pictures of people doing it, or even just pictures of naked women, never did do a whole lot for me. I never had even taken much interest in the fuck books—Maggie and Jiggs, Popeye and Olive Oyl, and so on—that always circulated in school at such high price.

So the very next day, our fourth morning at work, He come out stubborn again. For the first time, too, Miss Charlotte wanted to work in clay, which is, of its nature, a slower process than sketching in charcoal, and she got so impatient and upset I thought she was going to explode.

Her nice hand would get Him to a standing pose, all right; but by the time she'd start thumping at the lump of clay with her fists, He'd droop again. Which caused her to speak cuss words. I tell you, it was something else to hear that lady curse in her elegant,

53

clipped voice; she put thought into it, and imagination; and then finally she slapped down the handful of wet clay and came over to me.

With a sudden quick gesture, she knelt down and put her mouth on Him. Oh, my, that was something else! That was what He had been looking for! He throbbed up to full size, just as ready as ever in His lifetime, and when she went smiling back to her work stand, He held it for a good thirty minutes.

But the next time . . . well, it wasn't my fault, I don't believe. Of course, He did falter after that long while. This time she didn't hesitate, but came over, wiping her hands, to take the head gently between her lips, doing Him so lovingly it was just real nice, that's all, and He was throbbing and jumping all over again. But then, getting too experimental, she raked the raw edge of her teeth over the tender head—and He shot it so quick she barely had time to get her head out of the way.

"Now you've ruined it!" she snapped furiously. "The whole morning's work just shot to hell. For God's sake, boy, you must learn to control yourself."

"Well, you're being pretty mean to Him," I said, as mad as she was with me. "You just ain't treating Him right, Miss Charlotte. So what do you expect?"

She checked her anger. "What do you mean?"

"You just can't do Him no such a way," I told her. "You expect Him to stand ready for hours at a time, and yet you don't offer Him nothing for all His hard work. If He can't feel there's something good in the offing, why should He do your bidding?"

I shook my head at her. "No, sir, ma'am. You don't understand Him, not the least little bit. How can you expect to make such a great thing of Him as you say you're going to do, when you don't know how He looks on life?"

She sighed. "You're right, boy." She studied me

54

seriously. "You see, I haven't had anything to do with a man's cock for so many years." She was suddenly depressed. "Maybe I'm not the person meant to do this work. Maybe it's not in me. . . ."

"You can do it, Miss Charlotte," I said urgently. "You've just got to be patient, that's all, you've just got to learn His good times and His bad times. You've got to give Him the house room He deserves."

She sighed again. "I'll try. I'll try." She put one hand on the unfinished model she had been working at, mashed it into a shapeless lump that was nothing but clay. "We'll try again tomorrow."

"Now, there you go," I said. "Sometimes I think you don't *want* to understand Him."

She turned quickly toward me. "What do you mean? He just lost it, didn't He? He can't possibly . . ."

"You just come over here and do that nice thing again and see what He can do." I spoke with all the confidence in the world. "You'll see what I'm talking about. Why, Miss Charlotte, you've done woke Him up for good, giving Him a whole new interest in life."

She stared into my eyes. She came close, put her right hand under His head, gazed upon Him. He perked up, stirring in her palm with His own life, which she smiled to see. Then, very carefully, very gently, she kissed Him, putting the tip of her tongue into His eye to taste Him. He was nearly there already, just with the notion that in the next minute she was going to swallow Him whole.

She meant to do it. But first, making a bellows of her cheeks, she blew her warm breath on Him, until when she did take Him whole He was at a fuller stand than she had ever seen before.

So we worked happily the rest of the morning, and she got done a free-standing model of Him that seemed to satisfy her, at least to some extent.

When she wiped her hands and said she was

finished for the day, I stepped off the pedestal to put on my clothes.

"Wait a minute," she said. "Are you seeing one of your ladies this afternoon?"

"No, ma'am, I reckon not," I said.

She stood looking at me for a minute. "Then go over there and lie down on that daybed," she said. "I intend to let Him know there are rewards for all His labor."

Oh, He heard the news. I hadn't realized that He had yearned to get inside of Miss Charlotte. Hadn't really thought about it, to tell the truth, since she had told me all about how she liked women as well as I did. But of course He had kept His own notions, and He meant to do her proud.

However, Miss Charlotte had something else in mind. Without taking off her clothes, she laid herself down between my legs and treated Him for about ten minutes to the best blow-job it had ever been His fortune to enjoy. She just put Mr. William in the shade in that department, though maybe that was because she was a woman after all, even if a lesbian, and I had always felt a mite uneasy about putting Him in the mouth of a man, nice as Mr. William was about it all; though nearly every time getting so excited he'd end up hurting Him a little, in spite of everything.

Miss Charlotte didn't get excited. But she made a fine job of it, I can tell you. And when it come to the end, she didn't back off, either, but took it most nicely, and stayed with Him in the afterpart when it's just the best of all. Then she snuggled her cheek into my crotch and laid so for a while, breathing deeply and saying, "You smell so nice. Did you know that you have a nice wonderful clean smell?"

She was sort of whispering the words, so they didn't need no answer. We laid so for some minutes, at peace with ourselves and at peace with Him.

Finally she got to her feet with her usual briskness. "This is all very pleasant, but you told me things today I must think about." She paused to look at me most thoughtfully. "I think I'll call Vi tonight, tell her to come on down and join me right away. I think . . . I think we need Vi to help us do the great thing we've set out to do."

The Girl

It was a whole week before I saw the bread-truck fellow again. It made me wonder, but when I asked about it, first chance I got, he said on other days he had other routes to run. Come Thursday again, though, and there he was. I had nearly reached the artesian well when he came rolling along; he didn't stop, but went to wait until I got there. Smiling secretly to myself, I took my time. I knew that silver quarter would keep.

He was standing in the open doors of the truck. He reached one hand to pull me up, and the minute the doors were closed, he grabbed me so tight I couldn't breathe. He laid his hands under my ass to hold me close, and he was kissing my face, just shaking all over. I let him do as he pleased for as much as a minute before I moved away.

"You know it's gonna take another quarter," I warned him.

58

"All right, all right," he said impatiently. His old Thing was bulging his pants something awful.

"Give it here, then," I said, holding out my hand.

He put a quarter into my palm. I looked at it, folded my hand tight, and placed my books on an empty shelf. I looked at the aisle between the shelves, pleased with what I saw. It had not only been swept clean, but there was a nice army blanket all spread out. So I just laid down backward, hiking my skirt and pushing down my drawers as I did so.

"Here It is," I said. "Come and get It."

He was so stirred up to gaze on my offered nakedness that he looked like he was going to be sick; his face was drawn, and his body was trembling like he had the chills and the fever. He didn't take time to pull off his white coveralls, either, but fell on me like a hawk on a chicken.

Lord, he was so frantic. I wrapped my arms around him, trying to soothe him down, talking, telling him he didn't have to be in no such a rush, there was all the time in the world because he had done paid his quarter, hadn't he? It didn't do no good. I reckon he was so caught up he didn't hear what I had to say; at least, he spurted it so quick It was over before he had hardly poked his old Thing at me. Then he just collapsed, his breath coming so hard I thought he was crying, like Papa always cried.

So I held him, though his used-up little old Thing had slipped out; and we lay so for a long time. Gradually I noticed that he was coming back to himself, so I reached down and found enough to tuck inside where it belonged to be. I cherished his Thing with my pussy while it grew and grew, and all the time he was gazing down into my eyes, feeling what I was doing to him. Remembering how much pleasure he had got out of it the time before, I put my mouth on his breast nipple. A ragged sound came from his throat. I held him with my legs so he couldn't hardly move and took it away from him like taking candy from a baby.

"Good God, girl, where did you learn to do It like that?" he asked after he was finished.

"I don't know," I said. "I just do It, that's all." Then I said, most reasonably, "After all, you've got to get your quarter's worth, ain't you?"

He sort of laughed, still holding me close and beginning to move his hips around, though as far as I could tell, he didn't have nothing left to do with. Then he started in to kissing me. I pushed him away, saying, "I think you've got It by now, so get up off of me."

He rolled to one side. But when I started to put my dress down, he said, "Wait a minute," and laid his hand between my legs. Well, that was nice of him to think of it, so I let him. He was watching my eyes while he twirled his hand. But when it started making me feel restless, like that sort of thing will do, I pushed his hand away with both my hands and covered myself.

"Don't you want something, too?" he asked, surprised.

"Don't you worry your head about me, mister," I told him. "Just worry about yourself." Then I looked at him sweetly. "Will you bring me another quarter next week?"

"Yes," he said. "Before then, if I can steal the time from another route."

So, knowing I had a steady income I could count on, I was proud of myself as I added the second quarter to the first quarter in my Reynolds-wrap-lined fruit jar; then a third and a fourth, making a whole dollar, both coming in the same week, because he was there on the Tuesday and again on the Thursday.

But I want to tell you, men are hard to deal with. Seems like they ain't never satisfied with what they got. Here he had a nice girl he could count on, and he seemed to like It better every time he came. But it wasn't enough, no sir, he had to start talking about me sneaking out at night so's he could carry me to his place, where we could take off all our clothes and get into a real bed together. The first time he mentioned it, I told him nothing doing right off, because I didn't aim to try no such trick on my papa.

"He'd whale the tar out of me," I said. "You might just as well not talk about it anymore."

He wouldn't shut up about it, though, so that finally I had to say, "If you mention any such a nasty thing to me one more time, I won't take no more of your money. I'll walk right on by your old bread truck with my head held high."

He got a hurt look to his face. "But can't you see that I . . ." He stopped for a minute. Then he said, "Listen. I live all to myself in a house trailer. Air-conditioning and everything, with inside bathroom and running hot water and a color television. You'd like it there, you really would, and when I'd come home from work at night, we could . . ."

"You talking about me *living* with you?"

He got an eager look. "Will you do it? I love you, girl, I guess you know that, and I know you like me, else you couldn't be so good doing It with me. You know you like It as much as I do."

Maybe I gave him to believe I was thinking about his idea, because I didn't say anything for a minute. His face got all lit up, and he was holding my arms hard with both hands, and he was starting to shake like he did when I had first raised my skirts for him.

"Get your clothes together and run away tonight. I'll meet you here in my own car to take you home. Oh, love, you'll like living with me . . . we'll be so wonderful together. . . ."

I shook my head. "I don't want to live with you," I said. "First thing you know, you wouldn't want to pay me no more."

61

He stopped dead still, like he hadn't heard aright. Maybe he didn't want to hear what I was telling him. Then he got this very serious expression on his face.

"I'll marry you," he whispered. "I'll make you my wife."

Well, that did it. Making him let go of my arms, I moved a step away. "Mister," I said, "I ain't but fourteen years old. That ain't old enough to even begin to think about getting married."

His face was all twisted up with the hard begging. "But I love you. You must love me. Like me, anyway, and once we're married . . ."

"I don't know nothing about no love," I said. "All I want is my quarters. That's all I've got on my mind."

Turn a fellow down and he'll get mean on you every time. He glared. "You're just a two-bit whore. That's all you are," he snarled.

"That's not nice," I said, my voice as sharp as a slap in the face. "If you can't do nothing but talk bad-mouth to me, I'm going home."

I picked up my books and marched right out of that bread truck, him trying to stop me, saying he was sorry, he hadn't meant a word of it, please don't go away mad. But I reckon I know when I've been insulted. So I wouldn't be denied.

He leaned out after me. "Will I see you again?" he said, his voice as tangled as his suffering face.

Mad as a hornet though I was, I had to take some pity. "As long as you got a quarter in your pocket, I'll be here right on time," I said. I couldn't help but add, "But I ain't going to feel half so nice about it, I'll tell you that, not after what you said to me."

I reckon, though, the more he thought about it, the madder he got. I know it for a fact that he meant to do me dirt. I suppose he had to prove to his own satisfaction that he couldn't possibly be in love with a girl who'd do It for a quarter. I don't know. Sometimes men are hard to understand, except when they've got a hard-on and only It on their minds. Then they're just as clear as glass.

Be that as it may, the very next day, when I come switching my tail home from school, a stranger was waiting at the artesian well. Sitting in the front seat of a big old Cadillac automobile, he had the door open to put his feet to the ground. When he saw me coming, he started to twirling a quarter, tossing it into the air and catching it while looking at me instead of the quarter.

I come close, then stopped.

"Come here, little girl," he said.

I moved nearer still. He was a short little fellow, hardly taller than me, but fat, so that he was wide, too. His belly just bulged out over his belt buckle. His skin was real dark, and his cheeks were fat and hanging down on each side of a small mouth. His nose was large and strong in the middle of all that fat. He was wearing a nice blue suit with a red necktie, and he was sweating in the heat.

Still tossing the coin, turning sparkling in the air, he said, "Want to make yourself a nice shiny quarter, girlie?"

"Where'd you find out about me?" I said.

"Fellow drives a truck for me kept bragging about this piece of tail he had stashed out here on this byroad," he said. "So I thought I'd take a look-see for myself." His eyes, in their folds of fat, showing no bigger than a penny, were bright and greedy.

"You ain't been drinking, have you?" I said.

"Never drink anything but a little wine with my meals," he said, surprised. "What makes you think I'm drunk?"

"It's just that I can't stand the smell of liquor," I said.

"Well, what about It? Want this quarter?"

63

"Yes, sir, I reckon so," I said. I smiled. It was the first time I had felt like smiling at him. "Ain't never turned down a quarter till yet."

"Then come here." He moved his legs, expecting me to walk between them. I didn't move.

"Give me the quarter first."

"That's what I want to do. So come here and let me give you your money."

I went closer. He reached out his short arm, holding the quarter between two fingers over the square neck of my dress. When he let go, it dropped cold into my bra. He watched the expression on my face, then put one hand to my backside and the other one flat against my pussy. I had expected him to be rough, maybe even nasty about it, but he just rubbed me nice and easy.

When he was satisfied that I wouldn't flinch, he dropped his hand to go up under my skirt, and went on that way for another minute or two. I expected him next to seek my nakedness under the flour-sack drawers, but instead he stopped entirely, saying, "Get in the back seat, girlie. I'll be with you in a minute."

I got into the back seat. He looked up and down the empty road—hardly ever any traffic along here—and then got all the way inside and closed the door. He drove the car behind an overhang of vines, hiding it entirely from the road. Made me wonder why the bread-truck fellow hadn't thought of such a thing; but then, nobody's going to pay attention to a bread truck parked alongside the road, while anybody in the world would take note of a Cadillac.

"I want you naked by the time I get there," he said. He was busy getting out of his own clothes.

"I ain't taking off my dress," I said. "That ain't in the bargain."

"Either take it off or I tear it off," he said, as calm as you please.

I couldn't have that, could I? . . . How would I

get home? I could just see Papa's face if I come truck-
ing in as naked as a jaybird. So I wriggled around
and got out of my clothes, feeling the nice car seat
cool and rough on my naked skin.

Leaving the motor running and the air-conditioning on, making it as cool as a body could ask for—it
was real thoughty of him, I decided, so then and there
I started in to liking him—he got naked into the
back seat beside me.

But, Lord, he was *so* fat and *so* hairy, thick black
hair curling all over his belly, with a swath broaden-
ing out over his chest; and though he was short, he
seemed to fill the whole back seat. When I got a look
at his old Thing, it was so tiny, nestled in all that thick
black hair, it looked like something a cute little boy
would wave at a cute little girl. I never had liked the
idea of a boy, so I wasn't sure yet that I was going to
enjoy earning this particular quarter.

He kneeled beside me, gazing on my nakedness.
"Nothing in the world like a beautiful young girl," he
said softly. "Oh, you are lovely, my dear. Lovely."

I was lying on the seat, one leg dropped to the
floor. Because I wasn't no bigger than a minute, I was
so comfortable and cool I could have gone to sleep. I
lay still, letting him feast his eyes—which he did to
his heart's content before finally he touched my
breast, then stroked his hand down my belly to my
crotch. Back again to my breast, then another stroke,
like petting a cat. His hand was soft, so gentle, I began to like him all over again, so that I smiled, sleepy-
like, and he started whispering, "Oh, yes, you like It,
don't you, lovely child, the touch of a man on your
body, oh, yes, lovely, lovely. . . ."

It was funny, but his voice had changed, taking
on a singsong sort of accent, and part of the time he
was talking in a foreign language I didn't know. But
that was only after he had snugged his hand between
my legs and glued his mouth to the nipple of my

65

breast, so that when he pulled away to talk I could feel the warm breath of his words.

I let him do as he pleased until it began to make me restless. So I stirred myself out from under the petting, saying to him, "I ain't got all day, mister."

He leaned back for a moment, smiling. "There is no time, my dear, at a time like this. Don't think about time."

He went on about his business. As he got himself up over me, I saw that his old Thing had stayed short in getting hard, but had thickened up considerably. Then I didn't have time to think about it, because he had it inside of me, and I was smothering under all his fat, so that I had to struggle to draw air.

Well, I want to tell you something. He might have been so fat and hairy you'd have thought he was a bear instead of a man. But when it come to fucking, he just put the bread-truck fellow in the shade.

He started slow and easy, moving an inch back and an inch forth, slow and easy, slow and easy, rocking himself into me. In no time at all, I was rocking with him, because, taking so long to get started, I figured It would be soon over. I had figured wrong. He was right about there being no time in doing It; he just kept on and on and on, going stronger as he traveled his road, and I want to tell you, a girl can't stand that sort of thing forever, which was how long he looked like making It last. I couldn't breathe, his weight so heavy on me, and I was getting so stirred up I didn't hardly know what to do with myself. So I guess I got sort of desperate to get It done with.

Be that as it may, I just grabbed his old Thing, there inside of me, and started milking. I had to finish him and get his Thing out of my pussy before I just died. He grunted and said something in that foreign tongue of his—Greek, I found out later, he was a Greek—and buried his face in my neck and held his Thing stiff and still and let me have my way. He didn't move even when his Thing started throbbing and gushing, and so that part of It, too, seemed like lasting forever before I had taken all he had to give.

He was kind enough to get right up off of me. Staring at me, he wiped the sweat of honest labor from his brow. Then he smiled, just a beautiful smile, and laid his hand into my neck.

"My dear, you are a great courtesan," he said, His fat belly, the sweat gleaming on it, shook with sudden laughing. "And all for the price of a quarter, the one-fourth part of a dollar."

"What did I do?" I said, interested as I could be. I didn't exactly understand what he meant by calling me "a great courtesan," but it didn't sound nasty and mean at all.

"You don't know what it is you do?" he asked, showing surprise. "My dear child." He slapped his forehead with the flat of his hand. "You have, in absolute ignorance, given me a joy I have not experienced since coming to America. It is a thing American women do not seem to learn . . . nor many European women, for that matter."

"Thank you," I said, though not understanding in the least what he was talking about.

He leaned over to kiss me. Not wishing to get It started again, you understand, just a friendly kiss, so nice, and I liked it so much I put my arms around his neck to hug him. He kissed me again, then pulled away, saying, "You have a great talent, lovely girl. Don't waste it."

So I laughed and said, "I don't aim to. Not as long as there are quarters to be had." I kissed him again, of my own free will, and said, "I got to go now. I need to get the house cleaned up before Papa comes home."

He didn't argue; he climbed out of the back seat and got into the front so I'd have room to get dressed in comfort. As I slid out of the car, books in my arms,

I stopped long enough to tell him sincerely, "Mister, you're *nice*. I hope you'll come see me again."

He smiled. "Don't think I won't, child. Don't think I won't."

I'll tell you, it is something nice to be a success in this world. Within the next couple of weeks, it wasn't just a matter of the bread-truck driver—he did come back, though with a hangdog look when he saw what he had started with all his bragging—and of Mr. Greek (that's what I always called him, because I couldn't twist my tongue around his foreign name); why, sometimes there would be as many as four or five men waiting at the artesian well when I came prissing along on my way home from school.

It got to be a regular party. Why, those fellows would bring Cokes and beer—I wouldn't allow no whiskey drinking, let me tell you that—and maybe hamburgers and hot dogs, too, and they'd be sitting there just as friendly, talking and waiting and having their eats and drinks. The minute I arrived, though, there wasn't but the one thing on their minds.

Of course, they tried to make it a problem as to who got to go first. But I took care of that right quick. I just let them know I'd make my choice to suit myself, and if they didn't like it, they could lump it.

First thing, I'd go around to kiss each and every one. The order in which I kissed them let them know how I'd made up my mind to do It that particular day. Like, the first time the bread-truck fellow came around again, just as sheepish and embarrassed as could be to see the other men—and just a little dikty about it, too—I made him wait until dead last just as a punishment, though, truth to tell, I was grateful that he had advertised me enough to tell all these other customers.

Next I'd pick out my vehicle. Sometimes it was the bread truck, sometimes it was Mr. Greek's big Cadillac; best of all, though, was a big camper belonging to a lean, tough fellow, which had an air mattress fitted to the floor. When I climbed in, they started coming with their quarters.

It was an education, all right. Right there, at that artesian well, I learned about men. I found out there ain't no two alike, so that a girl has got to pay attention to their needs and wants, because sometimes they don't even know themselves, or are ashamed to say.

Mr. Greek was the best of the lot when it come right down to fucking. He was always so nice, so gentle, yet seemed to last forever, even if he was as fat as a pig, and never needed to draw his second wind; besides, he had a silver tongue in his head to praise a girl with, so that he made me feel pretty good just with his talking.

The lean, tough fellow who owned the camper wasn't no slouch, either, even if he was mighty rough. It seemed like he aimed to stab me to death with his old Thing, and when he got into the throes, he'd start beating at my head with his doubled-up fist, so that I had to turn pretty dodgy to keep from getting bruised. Afterward, though, he'd say he was sorry in just the sweetest words a girl could ever hear, and tell me how his wife was cold as an old boiled potato, and if he wanted any, he had to take It away from her.

Just all kinds of fellows. One young man, quiet and sweet, didn't want nothing but to talk whilst I held his Thing in my hand. Didn't ever even take off his clothes; and not only told me about all sorts of things, but recited poetry that I thought he was making up out of his own head until he told me he had memorized hundreds of beautiful poems. When he couldn't sleep of a night, he said, he'd hold his Thing in his hand and run through his mind the most beautiful love poems in the English language. He liked it a lot better, though, for me to do the hold-

69

ing. I tell you, I learned more fine English poetry from him than ever I did in the classroom.

One fellow, all he wanted was to take dirty pictures. Brought all this fancy camera equipment, lights and everything, but I wasn't having any of that; told him straight out in no uncertain terms that I didn't want men gazing on my body when they couldn't touch me, because all they'd do then was think dirty thoughts. He offered me as much as a dollar to pose for him, and then when I turned him down, he got pretty horsy. I just marched naked to the door of the camper and called to the fellows still waiting that I figured I needed a little bit of help. They got rid of him, all right; in such a way as he wouldn't feel free to come back.

The good word must have just kept spreading, because nearly every day I'd see the face of a stranger. I didn't mind in the least; those quarters just kept filling up the fruit jar. It got to where I had so much business to tend to I had to start getting up early in the morning to clean up the house, so I'd have time enough in the afternoon at the artesian well.

Now, let me tell you, at that time in my life I didn't know the first thing about protecting myself. So you may wonder how it was that I got by without being knocked up to have a baby. Lord knows, they run enough of that baby-making stuff through me. I just didn't worry about it, that's all; I remember my mama telling, once, that to her way of thinking a woman took a baby when something in her body or her soul *wanted* to get caught. So I just made up my mind to it, and never had a speck of trouble. Ain't never had no trouble in that way, for that matter.

It got to where I was a pretty tired little girl come the time when I had finished with the last man and toted my shiny quarters home to put secretly in the fruit jar. But I was contented with life, except that

70

the same old problem kept cropping up with one or another of the fellows.

It was that, after a while, they couldn't rest content with the good thing they had found; each and every one decided, sooner or later, to cut out everybody else and have me all to himself.

Of course, the preacher who started coming twice a week, on Tuesdays and Wednesdays, didn't count, because that was just his way, you see, to remonstrate with me for my way of life, even to get down on his knees and pray for my soul to be washed white in the blood of the Lamb so that I would know the sinfulness of my ways and walk the straight and narrow path forevermore, to end up beside the shining throne. That was only his way, like reciting poetry was that other fellow's, because after he was through praying, he wanted me to get down on my hands and knees so he could do it dog-fashion, saying he couldn't stand to gaze into my beautiful, sinful face whilst he yielded himself to the old devil nature that dwelled so hard and strong in his polluted body. So I didn't pay him any mind.

But take Mr. Greek, now, he got serious; decided I ought to move to Pass Robin, work in his bakery during the day and keep house for him at night. He got to where he talked about it all the time, describing the pretty clothes he would buy me, the good life I would lead, and how we could have whole nights together two or three times a week, and he'd just love me to death and keep on paying me, too, more money than I'd ever dreamed of.

I couldn't take to that way of doing. Truth to tell, I *liked* all those different fellows taking their pleasure of me. So every time he'd tempt me, I'd think about never seeing the bread-truck driver again, or the nice fellow who told me all the good poetry, or even the fellow that never put it in me—he just liked

71

me to suck on his Thing, and when I didn't know what he meant, he showed me, and I swear, you never saw a man enjoying something so much in your life. Though I told him looked like he could find a bull calf to do him in that manner.

So finally, one day, I let Mr. Greek know that if he couldn't stop talking about carrying me to town I wouldn't let him come back again, ever. That did serve to shut him up. After a while. First he had to tell me how he had come to love me; meant it, too, because his voice was shaking with the words, and as he kissed me with greedy, nibbling kisses, his face was wet with his tears. Told me he had never in his life known a woman so lovely as me, so warm, and I had to love him too just because of the way I did It with him. I let him know that I did my dead level best with everybody and I just couldn't see it as right to cut out the other fellows and let him have It all.

So he shut up about tempting me to run away from home. But he wasn't the first or the last to try it. When I didn't have the first intention of quitting such a nice trade as I was doing. Why, by the time school let out, I had the quart fruit jar full and had started another one. This one, I knew, would fill up even faster, because, actually, school being over made it all that much easier. I could lay around the house all morning, thinking about how good the second half of my day would be; then, after lunch, I'd bathe and dress and fix my hair and take a walk down to the artesian well.

By now I needed the entire afternoon to tend to business. Maybe only one or two fellows would be waiting, but by the time I got started, others would be arriving, in cars and trucks and pickup trucks, and even once in a while one of those great big semis driven cross-country by a trucker. They had got the word, too, and come out of their way. Somebody even installed a picnic table in the shady spot hidden

72

from the road, and the fellows would be playing cards or dominoes, just as friendly as a club, you know, and so I'd kiss them one by one and start to work.

Didn't a man jack go away dissatisfied, either, feeling like he hadn't got his quarter's worth. It did this girl's heart good, I want you to know, to see the glow in their eyes as they raised up off of me. It didn't matter that another fellow had marched in front of him and somebody else was waiting behind; they each and every one believed in their hearts—they told me so many and many a time—that I gave him the best.

It may sound like bragging, but it's the truth. Just like Mr. Greek had told me a thousand times over, I was born to be what he called a courtesan. It wasn't a thing I had to think about; it was just that my sweet little pussy knew what it was the men wanted, and was willing and eager to give it. I can't describe it; they would come with their awful weight on me, and there would be in me every time an answer to the question they asked in all their different ways of asking, boldly or shamefully or timidly as the case may be.

I just knew. That's all. There was the one fellow who wanted me still and quiet, the one fellow who wanted me to bang off the minute he got in me —at least play like banging off, but when you just do It, who's to say whether it's for play or it's for real? Another fellow wanted me to act like I didn't aim to let him have It, to the point where he'd have to chase me and pin me down and take It away from me. I just knew these things, you see, I just did these things. And pleased them.

So I had the second fruit jar full of quarters and was well started on the third on the day when, just wore out from the ten fellows I had took care of that afternoon, I opened the door one last time, thinking to myself I'd better hurry because Papa would be coming home from work . . . and saw Papa standing there with his quarter in his hand!

It was a shock. I stood naked of body, staring down into his face, whilst, recognizing his onliest daughter, his face went white as bone.

"Papa," I said, backing away.

He come into the camper in one jump. "So it's you," he said. "You I've been told about that I can fuck for a quarter."

His long arm reached out. His hand took a hold of me. And I was afraid like I hadn't ever been afraid of him before.

The Boy

I reckon I was as much of a surprise to Vi as Vi was to me. I had got into the habit of entering through a door that opened directly onto the sun porch. Since Charlotte was ready to work at the stroke of eight o'clock in the morning, today, like always, I took off my clothes so I'd be ready for her.

As I turned around from folding my pants neatly in a chair, I saw the girl lying full length in a long chair. I stood buck naked, gazing at her whilst she stared back at me.

Finally she said, "So you're him," with a jerk of her head toward the statue.

"Part of him, at least," I said.

She got up out of the chair, laughing. "Yes. I can see which part."

She had long hands, and a colorless face in which the large eyes were also pale. There was length to her body, the waist willowy, her neck curved like

75

the neck of a swan. She was wearing a denim skirt and a halter top, and her thin feet were bare.

I say "girl" because she was much younger than Miss Charlotte; no more than thirty, I would say, though I'm not much to tell the age of a woman. Even the way she walked, as she circled me inspecting my body front and rear, was lazy, as though she were so tired she wasn't sure she could take the next step.

"I can see what Charlotte was talking about," she said, coming before me to look into my face. A worry crease showed between her pale, corner-tilted eyes. "But I don't understand why she felt it necessary to have me on the scene."

"Maybe she just wanted to see you," I said politely.

She gave me a look out of the edge of her eye. "Oh, yes, she *wanted* to see me, all right. We're lovers, you know."

She wasn't English, like Miss Charlotte. I couldn't tell much about her accent. She wasn't from around Pass Robin, though.

"Yes'm," I said. "I know."

"Isn't the idea shocking to a Gulf Coast redneck like you?"

"No'm," I said politely. "I reckon not."

"We've been together for a long time," she said in a secure sort of voice. "Five years, almost." She stopped talking. Her eyes were on Him, where He hung waiting to take His pose when Miss Charlotte came. "Do you know how women make love to each other?"

"Yes'm," I said. "Miss Charlotte told me all about it."

Her pale eyes having caught a deep glow, suddenly she was prettier. "We were home from the airport by eight o'clock last night, and we didn't get to sleep until three this morning. It was . . . lovely." She

76

kept watching me for some sort of reaction to the ideas she was planting in my head. "What do you think about that?"

"It must be nice," I said.

"Is that all you've got to say?" She laughed, sort of nastily. "Don't you think it's a terrible waste, for two lovely women to deny men the abuse of their bodies?"

"I reckon people do whatever it is they like the best," I said, calmly refusing to get into an argument. I moved my shoulders. "If it's what turns you on, who am I to say you nay?"

She sneered at me. "But, like any man, you secretly believe I'd a lot rather have you. Isn't that it? Let me tell you, Johnny Stud, a man doesn't know what love can be."

"I ain't no stud," I said, wishing Charlotte would come on. For the first time, she was running late.

To my relief, here she came. "Well, hello," she said. "Are you two getting acquainted?"

"Yes'm," I said. "I reckon so," watching while Miss Charlotte went to put her arms around Vi and kiss her on the mouth. They stood holding each other, smiling, their bodies so close you couldn't tell where the one left off and the other began.

"Did you get enough sleep?" Charlotte said tenderly.

Vi yawned. "Oh, I'll take a nap after a while, while you're working."

Charlotte turned toward me. "Well, what do you think, Vi? Isn't he all I said he was?"

The two lesbian women were studying me with cool eyes. It didn't bother me; by now I had got used to Miss Charlotte's ways.

Vi shrugged. "It's a fine cock, if you care for that sort of thing." I wanted to tell her He wasn't an It, but I didn't.

77

Charlotte got intense. "Oh, better than that, Vi. He's the immortal cock of the world. At least, He will be when I get through with Him."

She came close, put the flat of her hand on my hip, stroking down my flank to grip His head in a tender hand. "But to do such a great work, Vi, I must know Him inside and out, be able to sketch Him in my sleep. I thought it would be simple, but it isn't, Vi, there are terrible complexities, it's Thing and Idea, and physical and spiritual, all very simple and yet so terribly complex. I'm still learning Him, Vi. The deeper I go, the deeper I have to go."

She was so stirred up by the talking, she had taken away her hand and was pacing back and forth, one fist clenched in her effort to make Vi understand.

"That's why I had to have you, Vi. You must help me understand, help me see, help me to create the great thing I shall create out of Him. Do you understand, Vi?"

"Oh, Charlotte, you always get so carried away with your work," Vi said in her lazy voice. She looked at me. She looked back at Charlotte. "You know I've always admired what you do. But I've never been able to help you with it."

"This time, though, you *can* help." Miss Charlotte paused. "You're going to fuck this cock for me, Vi. Understand? You will take Him into your body, you will know Him, you will use Him like He was meant to be used."

"For God's sake, Charlotte!" The girl was truly shocked. "If I'd known that was what you had in mind, I wouldn't have got on that plane. You know I hate the very idea of a man."

"Vi, you're bi, and don't deny it," Charlotte said.

"I used to be," Vi said deeply. "Before I met you. But now . . ." She put her arms around Charlotte, holding her fiercely. "I can't even *think* about a man now. The very idea makes me ill. . . ." Her whole

78

body shuddered with disgust, while she clung to her lover like a little lost girl.

Charlotte hugged her. "If you love me, you'll do it for me," she begged. "I must have your help. Not just to know Him, understand Him, feel Him . . . there's also the physical problem of keeping Him on His toes. I can't work with anything less than a full erection, you see, and, like the boy says, He's got a mind of His own. I've done everything I can think of to keep Him interested. But it gets more difficult every day."

"No," Vi said, stubbornness edging her voice. "I won't do it. You can't make me."

Charlotte caught her by the waist, turned her facing her, looked deeply into her eyes. "Do you love me?"

"Yes," Vi said slowly. "You know I do."

"Then you'll do it. For me." She took a deep breath. "You will sit quietly and watch while we work. While you watch, you will hold in your mind what it will feel like to have Him plunging into you. You will desire it deeply, you will feel it truly. And then . . . when we're through posing for the day, you will fuck Him, you will suck Him, you will do all the things a man and a woman do together. While I observe, while I learn . . . and it will also be a reward for Him. . . ."

She paused triumphantly, looking now at me. "See? Look, Vi. He's already up and ready, just hearing what's going to happen. I didn't even have to touch Him."

I looked down. It was true. His head was red and throbbing, He was jerking impatiently, thrusting toward the pale girl with that mind of His own.

Charlotte, forgetting the talk, hurried to her work place and began slapping the clay, shaping it, building it, her eyes so greedy on Him I could practically feel their burning.

79

"Oh, that's lovely, that's the best yet," she breathed. "That's what I needed, oh, yes!" She glanced at her friend. "Just sit down over there, Vi, and do like I said. Look at this wonderful cock, think about Him, know you're going to use Him. . . . Oh, yes, lovely, wonderful, marvelous. . . ." Her hands were building the best modeling of Him she had done yet; even I could tell that.

Vi went obediently to sit on the edge of the long chair. I reckoned she must know, by now, how important it was to her friend to make her great work of art, for she did what she had been told to do. While I stood looking at her, her long hands and her long feet, and all the body in between, thinking that I hadn't ever had nothing to do with a woman who didn't want to have anything to do with me. I kept wondering how it would turn out to be.

Charlotte knew what she was doing, all right, when she had called Vi into the picture. He kept His stand longer than ever before, without her having to stop work to keep Him that way. I wondered why it was He could stay so damned ready for something that didn't want Him in the first place. But that's just how contrary He could be; the more I thought about it, the warmer I got, because it would just have to be different from anything me and Him had ever experienced. My old ladies, one and all, they was so greedy He hardly had time to get ready before they had jumped Him like a mad dog on a bone. Oh, she would be cold and slow, I knew it as well as anything, and she would make up her mind to hate every minute of it. But He had the confidence in Himself, you see; just let Him get in there and root around, He'd make a place for Himself, all right.

After the longest time, of course, He finally eased off the peak of expectation; you can't expect a fellow to live on hope alone. The minute she noticed, Miss

Charlotte stopped in her feverish work and stepped back, tired but happy.

"It's the best yet," she muttered. "Can't quit now, I've got to finish it, got to be able to look at it whole, visualize how it will go with the statue." She raised her head. "Vi, take off your clothes."

"Charlotte!"

"Please. You must! Please."

With such raggedness of begging in her voice, Vi could do aught else but what Miss Charlotte asked. Standing, she began slowly unfastening the halter. She showed me small breasts, with very large nipples, shaped like a pear is shaped, and well separated one from the other. Her rib cage was bony, so thin I could see her breathing. He began to perk up again.

She unfastened the belt of her denim wraparound, let it fall to the floor. Didn't have on anything under it, which was a nice surprise; He sprang to attention at the very idea that she had been sitting there all this time as naked as a jaybird under her dress.

Her body was a surprise, too. Though I had viewed her as thin and bony, her belly and hips showed a surprising lushness. Her flanks were wide though thin, with nice shadings down into the bush of hair. And that was just the finest surprise of all; black and very thick, like a mat between her legs, square across the top like a woman is but running down the insides of her thighs because it hadn't been trimmed in the longest time. The hair of her head was pale gold, long and straight to her shoulders, and I wondered how she could have black hair in one place and pale gold another. Maybe she tinted one or the other, I don't know.

So I stood there looking, thinking about what was hidden behind that enormously thick bush, and Charlotte was back at work again, not frantic to build this

81

time, but slow and delicate, concentrating on the tiny shapings and sculpturings that suddenly made the clay into a cock that was realer than real.

"Go close and touch Him," she said. "Just touch Him now, Vi."

"I don't think I have to," Vi said, making a small laugh. Then she did a strange thing. She had been looking at Him, like I had been looking at her, with the sort of fascination she hadn't shown before. Suddenly, though, she bit her lip and raised her eyes to my eyes. Gazing directly into me, a look crossed her face like unto a stroke of pain running deep through her body.

She turned her head quickly, and wouldn't look at me again until Miss Charlotte stopped, standing empty as she gazed upon her work.

"It's good, isn't it?" she said, "It's very good."

Vi went to inspect the piece. "Yes," she said. "Yes, it is."

Charlotte, so pleased with the quiet words, put one hand warmly on her friend's arm. "Thank you, Vi," she said. "You understand now, don't you?"

"As much as anyone who isn't an artist *can* understand," Vi said.

They were so close, I was just left out in the cold. But then Miss Charlotte, putting her arm around her friend's waist, turned Vi's naked body toward me.

"All right. The rest of it now."

"It's not necessary now, is it?" the girl said, her voice rising on a note of panic. "The work is done."

"This is just a model. It must be done on the statue, you see, and I'm not ready yet for that. There'll be another preliminary model tomorrow, and the next day, and the next." Charlotte shook her head. "I don't know how long it'll be before I dare risk . . ."

"But you're through for the day, aren't you?" Vi, in her turn, was begging now, as Miss Charlotte had begged before. "So what difference does it make?"

"One can't make the promise and then break it, can one?" Charlotte said seriously. "That would ruin Him completely, don't you see that? Tomorrow He might well refuse entirely. One must, above all, be honest with a cock." She stood away from the girl. "I won't let you cheat, Vi. You must go through with it, because you let Him believe that you would."

Vi shuddered. "But . . . Charlotte . . ."

Charlotte turned to me. "Go over there and lie down. He's going to get fucked now. Just as promised."

Miss Charlotte had the Indian sign on Vi, all right; when Charlotte took her elbow, she came along meek as any lamb to gaze upon me laying ready on the daybed.

"I want you on top," Charlotte told the girl. She glanced at me. "You just lie there, let Vi do all the work. Is that all right?"

"Yes'm," I said. "However you want it, that's all right with me."

"Charlotte," Vi said in a voice that was raw with hurt. "You're really going to make me fuck this man?"

"I'll be right beside you, kneeling close enough to touch," Charlotte said softly. "Because I must see it, I must experience it with you, through you. . . ." She gave the girl a little push. "Go on now."

The girl slowly laid her naked body between my spread legs. The long hair fell down over her face, so that she pushed it to one side. Her eyes were wide and still as she gazed upon Him. I waited for her to look at me again, deep into my eyes like she had done before, but she wouldn't look into my face.

Instead she reached out a trembling hand to tilt Him ready. Her lip was bitten between upper and lower teeth, her face was suffering with the need to please her friend. With such cringing that I began to feel sorry for her, she lodged His head in the upper

83

part of her cunt, just barely touching. The instant she felt Him, she shuddered, turning her head pleadingly toward her lover.

Charlotte wouldn't be denied. Her eyes bright and seeing, she was beside us, close enough to put her hand into the small of the girl's back, pressing her down onto the greased pole of His enormous erection.

She took Him slowly, hurtingly, into a cunt as cold as ice. But she did take Him, deep and true, then lay stretched out absolutely still on top of me. She was taller than I was, so she laid her face into my shoulder to hide from my eyes . . . and maybe from Charlotte's. I kept as still as she did, feeling her tight and cold. Miss Charlotte's curious hand found my balls, making Him jerk.

"Fuck, Vi," Charlotte said urgently. "You must fuck Him, Vi."

Vi didn't answer to the command. Maybe she couldn't. She could only lay still, taking Him to the hilt like a knife into her guts, and on her cheek that touched my cheek I could feel the wetness of her tears.

Something moved inside of me. A feeling for the girl, yes, but also an excitement from knowing that she didn't want Him there. A sort of a rape, I reckon, and it did turn Him on. And me feeling, along with the lust, a pity that was close to love, so that I wanted to turn her under me, fuck her so nicely .that she'd be bound to answer to Him with everything that was in her to answer with.

I wasn't supposed to do any such as that, though, and I knew Miss Charlotte would put a stop to it right away. So I stroked her, there on the inside, without moving on the outside, just a tiny, gentle movement of His head to let her know He liked being where He was. Her body tightened, whether for it or against it I couldn't tell, so I stroked her again. I

84

hadn't known a fellow could fuck a woman without moving, but I was doing it; we were sreaking it on Charlotte, right enough, making love secretly on the inside while to all outward appearances we remained still and cold. Except that Miss Charlotte, with her hand warm to my balls, must have felt what I was doing to the girl; but somehow that didn't disturb in the least the secret closeness.

Vi was warming. She didn't want to, but there was a secret flow of wetness and of warmth, and suddenly her cheek was tight against my cheek. She understood the secretness, too, she welcomed it, she was letting me know she was there, too. So for the longest while I fucked her in that manner, until her pussy started working, too, not only answering Him but leading Him on.

"You mustn't just lie there, you know," Charlotte said from all the way out there in the outside world where we could scarcely hear her words. "You must do Him nicely, love, do Him nicely."

Vi raised her head, the arch of her neck sending a leverage through her long body that pressed us even closer, and looked into my eyes. In her eyes there showed a warm, small laughter that was the joke between me and her, a big joke against Charlotte way out there in the cold world, and all of a sudden, still holding cold on the outside, she came in a sudden gush of liquid warmth that just damn nigh drowned Him. I smiled, she smiled; it was such a wonderful secret to share.

Then, only then, she obeyed Charlotte's demand, sliding herself up and down the throbbing pole. Charlotte chuckled, saying, "That the girl, He's coming now, He's getting ready for it," because she still had her hand on my balls, you see, and could feel what was happening. Vi fucked, not wildly, but slowly, gently, lovingly, and when I came she took it with another

85

small secret coming of her own. Then she laid her body down on mind, and for the minute we were warm and close.

Charlotte slapped her hand on Vi's bare ass in a sudden cheerfulness. "Now. That wasn't so bad, was it?"

With the coarse words, I felt Vi's cunt tightening, turning cold. In a sudden movement, she rolled herself away and stood up. "I hated every minute of it," she said angrily and stalked naked out of the room.

I think she went away, though, because she didn't want to look at me; she didn't dare share the secret any longer, for fear Charlotte would see it too.

I'll tell you how I knew; the very next morning, the minute I came through the door, Vi was all over me, her long arms around me it seemed like two or three times, her mouth hot and frantic on my mouth, while she laid her hips so tight I could feel the shape of her pussy through the thin nightie.

"Come on, come on, hurry," she whispered between snatching one handful of kisses after the other. "Charlotte's still asleep, but we'd better hurry."

I just stood there. "We can't do that," I told her.

She pressed herself even closer. "Why not? It's our chance to do it by ourselves, without Charlotte hovering over us like a mother hen. Hurry." With an amazing strength of passion, she dragged me toward the daybed.

"But what about the posing?" I said. "He's got to be up and doing for that job of work."

"Who cares about that?" she said, whispering again. "Except Charlotte, I mean. You and I . . ."

I put my hands on her shoulders. "Now, listen here, girl," I said. "I don't aim to do nothing to ruin Charlotte's work, I'll tell you that here and now."

She stood for a second, gazing at me. "You mean you want it as bad as she does?"

"I sure do," I said. "Why, just think of it! After

86

I'm dead and gone, He'll be standing there forever for the whole world to admire."

She had quit listening at the first word. Because, going to her knees, her hands were busy at my belt buckle. She unzipped the pants, shoved them down, pushed down the Jockey shorts, and buried her face into my crotch.

"You've got to," she was saying over and over again. "I must have Him just once without Charlotte watching. I've . . ."

I put both hands tenderly on the top of her head. "So you liked Him after all," I said. "You really liked Him."

She gazed up wildly, both hands on Him now, stroking and petting. "Like Him?" she said. "Even when I was having men, I never found anything like Him." She put her face against Him, kissing Him, smelling Him deeply with deep breathings of her whole body. And let me tell you, that fellow knew He had won the woman!

"What are you doing, Vi?" Charlotte said from the doorway.

Vi stared frantically toward Charlotte. In a despairing move, knowing she had been caught out, she took Him into her mouth, pulling deeply to bring Him to full erection. Then, leaning away, she got slowly to her feet.

"He looked sort of lackadaisical this morning, so I was getting Him ready for you," she said, sauntering carelessly toward the long chair she liked to lie in.

"No need to be so frantic about it, is there?" Charlotte said dryly. "Couldn't you wait until the boy could get his clothes off, at least?"

"I *thought* I was doing you a favor, Charlotte," Vi said angrily.

Charlotte shook her head. "Vi, you always were bi, and you know it."

Vi flung around, her whole body flouncing inside

87

the thin nightgown. "Not since I met you, Charlotte, as you well know," she cried. "I've never been unfaithful to you, with man *or* woman. After all, fucking Him was your own big idea, wasn't it? It wasn't anything *I* wanted to do."

"You'll have Him again, Vi, don't worry about that. But you must wait until I'm through for the day." She turned to me. "Get your pants all the way off and let's get to work."

"I don't care," Vi said with sullen stubbornness. "It's all in aid of your art, you know."

That was how it went that day, Vi waiting sullen and silent as Charlotte worked. Because I was looking at her all the time, and remembering, there wasn't any problem about keeping Him at a stand, so Charlotte got a whole new model of Him, starting from scratch and finishing with the tiniest detail. It was a wonder how she could make the clay take shape and form from her strong hands; and this time, it seemed like, her hands were surer and swifter than ever before.

She worked so hard, so focused on the fruit of her hands, it was like she wasn't even in the room with us. Only once did He droop out of His conviction, at which Vi, with a wriggle of her body, simply pulled her nightgown up to her waist, so I could gaze upon the black bush that hid her treasure. It brought Him jerking to attention.

"Fine, Vi, that's just wonderful," Charlotte said in a faraway voice, her hands busy with the finishing touches, her thumbnail shaping the groove under the eye. Vi smiled, made a face, and put her hand down between her legs. He throbbed again, because all of a sudden our secret was alive again between us.

Charlotte stood back, wiping her hands on her apron. "All right, Vi, he's all yours now. Just let me wash my hands and I'll join you." Her head came up with an alert lift, so that I knew she'd been looking forward to reward time also. "I want you on top, and Vi on the bottom."

I want to tell you, she had to wash her hands and get there quick, because Vi was suddenly over on the daybed, shedding her nightgown as she went. As I moved to stand over her, looking down into her waiting face, she was lying long and straight, her legs together, her toes pointed. The big nipples were standing up, just ruby red with ardor, and there was a secret little catlike smile on her mouth.

She didn't move as I leaned down to her, so that I had to place my knees on the outside of her legs. She reached one hand to guide Him, her legs still tight together, so that He lodged and then had to push hard to get inside where He wanted to be.

"Damn it, wait a minute, you two, don't be in such a great hurry," Charlotte called.

Hurring though she was, by the time she got there He was already deep, and I want to tell you, it wasn't like yesterday, cold and flinchy, no sir, as Vi wrapped her long arms around my head to whisper into my ear, "All inside, like yesterday. All inside."

So I laid still, though on top this time, and stroked her throbbingly, whilst she made her secret answer, going immediately into the throes, the warmth and wetness gushing, and I nearly lost it myself because we had been waiting and thinking for such a long time now, with yesterday's memory to help us along.

The secret fucking was so strong in us, it didn't matter that Charlotte was sitting behind, where she could see my balls, and touch them, and stroke my ass whilst doing it. I gazed into Vi's slanty eyes; then I laid my mouth to her warm mouth, and she took my tongue as I began to fuck her with slow, easy strokes that opened her up. Yes, sir. With each down stroke she was open more, her legs parting and lifting and then locking into the small of my back, and she was going with me, saying, "Ah, aah, aaah," and we were

89

into it, rocking frantically, reaching deeper and deeper and hotter and hotter, until it all went off like a great big explosion and it wasn't a secret no more, no sir, you could have heard us all over the house, it was so wild and noisy.

"Now, Vi, you can't say you didn't like that," Charlotte's voice said from somewhere far off.

But she wasn't a part of us, not yet, because as I lay on the girl she began stroking Him inside, and before I could catch my breath, we were off again, sweeter this time and somehow nicer, and just so marvelous it made me think of all my old ladies rolled into one great big fuck.

That finished it, as far as I was concerned, but I wasn't anxious to leave her. Nor her to let me go; we lay looking into each other's eyes again, quiet now, smiling, and it didn't matter in the least that the secret was out.

I felt, then, the sting of Charlotte's hand on my bare buttock. I got up. Charlotte said, "I truly desired your cooperation, Vi, but I didn't expect you to be so wholehearted about it."

"What did you expect?" Vi said defiantly. "After all, you told me it was the greatest cock in the world."

"Yes," Charlotte said in a strange, tight voice. "Yes, He is, isn't He?"

I was busy finding my Jockey shorts, so I didn't know what was going on until I happened to turn around. Then I saw that Charlotte's head was between Vi's legs, her arms under Vi's ass to prop her up to it, and was just going to town with the licking and the loving. Vi glanced at me, smiling, and kept on smiling even as her legs locked strongly around her woman lover's head and her hips began to grind against the busy tongue.

When they were done, Vi just laid there like a

90

wrung-out dishrag. Charlotte turned on me most angrily, saying, "Well, I love the girl. Don't you see that I love the girl."

"Ma'am, it's all right with me," I assured her.

She smiled then. "Yes. I think it is," she said in her usual clipped tone of voice. We were as suddenly friends again as we had become jealous lovers of the same girl.

That was the beginning. In the days that followed, me and Vi got to make love when the modeling was finished with, and it didn't matter that Charlotte was right there with us, running the whole show. She made me fuck the girl every way a man can do a woman: dog fashion; with Vi sitting on my lap; standing up; with legs open and legs closed . . . you wouldn't believe all the inventions and variations I learned during that time. We even tried out some of the postures in that dirty book Miss Charlotte had showed me, and though I found a body can't be as limber as a snake, it can sometimes come peart nigh to it.

I also learned about women together, because every time me and Vi got through with each other, Charlotte had to make her run, too. It was not just mouth to pussy, either; Charlotte had what practically amounted to a little dick peeping out of her pussy, and could fuck the girl practically like I did. I must say, though I don't rightly understand how, they did seem to pleasure one another. I must admit, however much it sounds like bragging, that Vi, whilst making love with Charlotte, was always looking at me, remembering Him in the deeps of her eyes. Just no way to destroy that little secret we had started between ourselves without Miss Charlotte's knowing about it.

Afterward, they'd lie quietly in each other's arms. But, all the time, they were talking about Him. Charlotte asked ten thousand questions about how it felt to

91

have Him inside of her, how He compared with other cocks she had known, just everything; she wanted to know and smell and understand all there was about it. Vi, with patience and great understanding of the need that drove Charlotte into her great work, did her best. And, it seemed, told it awfully well, because, listening to them talk, He would come to a stand all over again with His own recollections.

So the work went well. Miss Charlotte happily made model after model, saying each one was better, and just any day now I expected her to begin modeling the last great final cock on the waiting sculpture.

Somehow or another, she didn't seem to get there, though with each passing day she spent more and more time gazing at the unfinished piece, walking around it, putting her hands here and there on its slopes and moldings. It was bothering her pretty bad; she got tighter of mind and grimmer of mouth, because she had expected, I could tell, to be able to do it by now, and it scared her that it wasn't there in her like she had counted on.

Come the day she didn't work with her hands at all. To all intents and purposes, she had gone as far as she could go with the separate modelings. So it was now or never; that was finished, but the next part, the sculpture itself, hadn't yet come to her.

She was in a tizzy, all right. She spent the morning pacing back and forth between me and the statue. She'd first feel Him, with careful, knowing fingers; then she'd put both hands to the statue, stroking it and stroking it. Then back once more to Him. She stroked my body, which she had not done before, her hands sliding over the slope of my ass and circling around my waist and down my legs all the way to my calves. Her hands were trying to learn the whole body, not just Him, which was what she had focused on before. She looked so puzzled, so hurt, that I just ached for her; Vi, sensing it too, stayed quiet and still.

Somehow, we knew, couldn't either one of us help Miss Charlotte anymore. Something inside of her, by her alone, had to be worked out. Suddenly me and the girl were strangers, because she was working in the deepest part of herself, digging hard, knowing that if she failed now, she would fail for all time, and the immortal cock would never be created. At least, not by her.

After it had gone on so for two or three hours, in which she looked older and tireder and scareder with each passing minute, she finally stopped halfway between me and the unfinished work. She looked from it to Him, and back again.

"I simply must face it, mustn't I?" she said quietly. "There really is but one way for a woman to know a man's cock." She gazed at the statue, she gazed at Him. "You must fuck me," she said, her voice so quiet and still it hurt to hear her.

"Charlotte!" Vi cried out.

Charlotte turned to her. "I've always said I'd do anything for my art, darling," she said gently. "I've never known until now just what that declaration could entail. But . . ."

Vi pouted. "You just want to fuck a man," she said like a jealous child, just absolutely refusing to understand what it was driving Miss Charlotte. "Don't try to kid me, lover. All this time you've been watching and wanting, haven't you? You *want* it, that great, nasty cock inside of you. . . ."

"You needn't see it if you'd rather not, darling." Quiet and still in voice, but I could see how shaken Charlotte was by her lover's jealousy. "But it shall happen. If it doesn't happen, I can't finish the work. It's as straightforward as that."

"You bitch, you can't fool me!" Vi said, putting

93

her hands to her face and beginning to cry. "It's all right if *I'm* bi, but you can't be too! You simply can't betray me. Maybe with another girl, a prettier girl, but not with a *man.* . . ."

But Charlotte was looking at me, I was looking at Charlotte, and suddenly Vi, in all her jealous tears, was nothing but a raging child somewhere way off yonder, nothing to do with two grown-up people in a grown-up world where great things get done.

I understood, you see. I reckon I had understood it all from the very moment Miss Charlotte had told me why she wanted to use Him as a model for the great cock of all time. Something in me, I do believe, had known it would have to come to this in the end, so that all the time she had been shaping and modeling clay I had been shaping and modeling myself— and Him—for the hour in which it would have to happen.

I understood; not in a thinking sort of way, you know, because I never have been much of a thinker. It was Billy, my twin brother who died of a fever when we were nine years old, who was the good thinker. Only in a feeling sort of way; though I had always counted Billy as the one of us two who had also *felt* things the best and truest. But it didn't matter, Billy was with me in both thinking and feeling in that moment when I did what I had to do, moving to Miss Charlotte and lifting her in my arms and taking her to the daybed.

As I carried her to the place where it would happen, she put both arms around my neck, clinging to me, and I was surprised by how light she was, how small in my arms. Beside the daybed, I stood her on her feet and began taking off her clothes. She waited quietly until at last she stood naked alongside my nakedness. I picked her up again; I kissed her deep and true; I laid her down.

94

She was like a warm doll under the strength of my hands. I had to lift her knees, open her thighs. She flinched, just once, when I put Him in her. Feeling the flinch, I eased Him slowly, very gently, but making her know Him every inch, insisting against the unwillingness of her flesh, until I lay deep and true.

I thought it was time to move then, but she laid a hand to each of my shoulders. "Be still," she whispered. "Let me feel Him. I must feel Him."

So I let her feel Him. Her eyes, her face, were far away. She was not cold, as Vi had been cold, but she was not warm, either. Once again I thought the time had come to fuck, but she stopped me again. "I must feel Him like a woman feels," she whispered. "It's very difficult. Very difficult. But I *must*."

I waited for her. After a very long time, a small smile came to her lips, and she said, "Yes. That's it, isn't it? He really *is* a lovely cock, isn't He?"

"The greatest in the world," I said, whispering too. "You told me He was. You were the one who knew."

"Yes," she said. "Yes. Of course." Taking her hands from my shoulders, she put them to each side of my face, holding my head to kiss me. Her mouth was cool, strange; I couldn't help but feel that it hadn't worked, couldn't work, because He wasn't, after all, what I, and Miss Charlotte, had believed Him to be.

Charlotte said, in a normally loud voice this time, "You can begin now. Begin, please."

I began. But I knew it had to be easy. If I failed now, Miss Charlotte would fail. And her flesh was so tender, so frightened of the manhood it had taken unto itself. So it took a long time, during which I fucked her with tiny movements, fearful of bruising her, hurting her, making her flinch again. Then, just a little bit stronger, a little bit longer, and she was trying —oh, yes, God—she was trying with all that was in
95

her. And suddenly it was like a high gate to a strong fort had clattered down to let in the enemy; she was truly feeling it, her flesh waking, and she gasped slightly, knowing, as I knew, that she had surrendered that which she had been holding back in spite of all desire to know Him to the hilt.

It took much time yet, faster and stronger and fiercer and without end, even when I lost it, a man being able to stand only so much, it banging out of Him into her. I heard her sigh of disappointment, so I whispered, "That's just for openers, we're just getting started now, it's not done with yet, not by a long shot," and she made a glad little sound.

She was wetter now, with my wetness, and warmer, and we built it all over again, until another gate went down, one we hadn't known about until it wasn't there anymore; and so, slowly, reluctantly, needfully, she became the woman to my man and started fucking me of her own accord, so that it was all there, solid and great, and she knew now, oh, yes, she knew, I could read in her hot flesh all the great knowing she had needed to know for the sake of her great work.

It was done, then, with me lying on her and her holding me in her arms, whispering, "Oh, my darling, my darling, my darling," her voice as soft and sweet and warm as her body.

But only for a minute, two minutes, before I knew she wanted me to take Him out of her body. I did so, reaching down to lift her to her feet. She came into my arms, huddling close and warm.

But only for another minute before she drew away, to show me a tearstained face and a trembling mouth. "You are a marvelous boy," she said. "With a marvelous cock. But of course you know that, don't you?"

"Yes'm," I said. "I know that."

"And more," she said fiercely. "So much more." She pushed at me with her hands. "Now, get away. Leave me alone. I must be alone."

I understood this, also. I hurried to put on my clothes and get out of her sight. As Charlotte went to her work place, she glanced carelessly at Vi and told her to get out too.

"Go make love to the boy, if that's what you want," she said. "But not here. Somewhere else."

We got out of there. But not before Charlotte commanded me not to go away, but wait outside until she called me. So I sat on a garden bench in the shade, watching Vi fidget and turn. She was still mad at both of us, just eaten up with jealousy.

Until finally she flung herself around, saying, "Well, if she can fuck you, so can I. Come on, we'll go to the bedroom." She made a nasty sound of her voice. "We'll do it where Charlotte and I sleep together."

"Vi, I can't do that," I said.

She put her hands on her hips, glaring at me. "What do you mean, you *can't* do it? You're a stud, aren't you?"

I shook my head. "I ain't no stud. And I can't do it, Vi. I'm sorry, but that's just how it is."

I knew I couldn't explain it to her. If I could have explained it, she couldn't have understood. Because she was nothing but an angry, jealous child. And maybe she didn't know whether to be jealous of me because of Miss Charlotte, or jealous of Miss Charlotte because of me.

The hours passed slowly. Noon came, hunger in my belly coming with it, but I didn't make a move to satisfy it. At some time or other, I don't know exactly when, Vi had disappeared into the house. She didn't come back, so I sat all by myself while the blazing Gulf Coast sun slanted toward the ending of the day.

It was near to the horizon when suddenly I raised my head to see Miss Charlotte standing across the garden. "You can come now," she said, in a voice so tired it was hard to believe.

I went to where she stood. Her shoulders were drooping; her face was empty. I touched her shoulder with one hand. "Is it done?"

"Yes," she said. "It is done. Come and see."

As we turned to go together, she put her arm around my waist, just as natural as could be. So I laid my arm to her waist, and together we walked to the sun porch, separating only to pass through the door. Then we stood together again, each touching the other, to gaze upon the finished work.

"It's all there, isn't it?" she said.

"Yes'm," I said. "It sure is."

"It's Him," she said. "And He is great."

"Yes," I said.

I can't tell you how I felt, looking upon what she had made. It had taken the all of her to do it—even the woman part of herself that she had fought so hard against having to use—but she had done it. And so, though I would come to death like all men, He would live on forever. A great Him.

"It's done now," she said, the tiredness showing again in her voice. "Of course, I must make the mold and cast Him in bronze. But that's only work, technique." She turned to me. "So I shan't see you again."

I looked at her. "But you'll have to see me. Won't you?"

"I shan't see you again," she said firmly. She walked away, taking away the nearness between us. "Before you go, I have something for you. I'll bring it."

She went away, to return quickly, trailed by a sad-looking Vi. Miss Charlotte had in her hands a golden chain, the links massive, heavy, as she lifted it over my head to hang against my chest.

"I made it myself," she said, smiling. "So you must keep it forever."

"I will," I said. "But . . ."

She stood on tiptoe to kiss me on the mouth. "Thank you, dear boy," she said softly. "You were all I wished you to be. And more. So much more."

"But . . ." I said.

She shook her head. "I'm quite satisfied with my life, darling." She made her voice sound light and easy with the words. She glanced at Vi. "Can't you see that?"

"But you won't be," I said. "And then I'll be gone."

She turned her head quickly. "Yes. You'll be gone." I didn't move. So she added, "It's over, dear boy. Finished. There is nothing between us anymore. We have done it all now, and it would be a mistake to try to keep on."

I thought about it for a while. Then I nodded, feeling sad. "Yes'm. I reckon so."

I turned to look at the statue again, to gaze upon Him one last time in all His everlasting life. I felt a happiness growing in me, taking the place of the sadness, so that I could smile too, now, and say, "We did it, didn't we, Charlotte?"

Her voice was happy. "Yes. We did it."

"Oh, God, you two," Vi said in a disgusted voice. "I'm going to punish you for this, Charlotte. Oh, boy, *how* I'm going to punish you."

"Yes, darling," Charlotte said quietly. "You *will* need to punish me, won't you?" She might as well have been talking to a child. Because she turned to me, smiling tenderly, and held out her hand. "Goodbye, boy. Go well."

I took her hand. "I will, Miss Charlotte. And . . . thank you."

There was more to say. But I couldn't say it. Because I was empty now. God, I couldn't begin to feel

99

how empty I was as I walked out of her workroom for the last time. There was nothing in front of me, nothing at all that I could see, or feel, or know about.

But little did I know that, so soon, the immortal cock I was leaving behind would bring me to an adventure the likes of which I had not known in my life up till then.

The Girl

I sure was glad all the fellows had already left when Papa marched me out of that camper, his hand gripped so hard on my arm I had the bruises to show for it. Once in the clear, he herded me home like a goose. I didn't dare look back to see his dark face; I hadn't ever known him to be so mad. Already the muscles in my butt were quivering; I knew it was just bound to be the worst whipping I'd ever taken at his hand.

He didn't say word one until we were home. I walked into the living room—cleaned up spick *and* span before I left that morning, I want you to know—and stood waiting.

"Turn around," he said.

I turned around. He looked at me. His eyes were just furious. He kept his voice low and mean, like he didn't dare let it get out of control.

"For better than a week, I been hearing all these

fellows talking about this pretty girl who'll do It with anybody for a quarter." He stopped, breathing hard. "So today, when I made up my mind I could use me a little piece of nooky my own self, being a widow-man and all, what do I find? My own sweet daughter. My own and onliest daughter, taking on all comers for two bits a throw."

He stopped talking to wipe his face with the flat of his big hand. I didn't say anything. He took a step toward me, causing me to flinch in spite of myself.

"How long has this been going on?" he said.

I didn't say anything.

He reached out to take hold of my arm again. "I asked you a question, girl."

I didn't say anything.

His face got like a thundercloud. He jerked me closer, his other hand rising to slap the tar out of me. But he didn't hit me. Not yet.

Instead he said, "What have you done with the money? Just frittered it away, I reckon, on pretties and doodads."

I didn't aim for a minute to let him think that. "I ain't," I cried out. "I ain't spent the first quarter. I've been a-saving it."

It stopped him. Then he said, "Where is it? I want to see it."

I figured he was trying to catch me out in a lie, and once he did, he'd just cut loose. So I marched into the bedroom, Papa following, and showed him the fruit jars. I tell you, there was a peculiar look to his face as he hefted the weighty jars filled to the brim with those fine quarters. One by one he spilled out the coins onto the bed, taking his time about it. There was a pretty pile of quarters, too, let me tell you, when he had emptied the last one.

His voice was quiet, even thoughtful. "Well. It looks like you've been working steady for some time."

102

"Yes, sir," I said proudly. "I ain't the one to brag, but let a fellow come once, he's bound to bring me another quarter every chance he can get."

I must have said just exactly the wrong thing. It made him rear back on his hind legs, more furious than ever. With both hands, he rech down to grab up a double handful of the quarters and fling them down onto the bedspread again. One of the coins bounced to the floor and rolled all the way into a corner, where it circled three times, making a thin, ringing sound, before falling over plop on its side.

"God Almighty, girl," he said. "If you just had the sense God give a goose, every one of them two bits might just as well be a dollar bill."

I stared at the pile of silver, thinking how if it was dollars instead. Doubtfully I shook my head. "A dollar is right much, Papa."

Oh, he got madder than a wet hen. "Take off your dress and look at yourself," he roared at me.

"Papa!" I said.

"Do like I said!" he yelled. "Damn it, or I'll . . ."

Now, I had there in the bedroom an old pier glass Papa had found once in a junkyard heap and brought home as a Christmas present. So I did like I was told, and stood looking at myself in the wavy glass.

He came up behind me. "Girl, there ain't a man in the wide world wouldn't pay a dollar for the chance to handle a pretty piece like that there," he said. "Now, ain't that the living truth?"

I looked upon myself, my pretty white hair and big blue eyes, that shade of blue I hadn't ever seen on anybody except my mama—I remembered, then, that the poetry-reading fellow had told me, once, they were Delft blue, a shade of color they use in pottery over across the big ocean, he said—and then at my breasts and my belly and my legs. I was ever just a pocket-piece of a girl, so tiny, but size

103

didn't matter, it was all there, and all ripe. I had even got to looking better from all the fucking I had been doing, because it's good for a girl's looks as long as she don't overdo It.

I had to admit it to myself; Papa was right. It was worth a dollar to have the using of a pretty girl like me. And here I had been practically giving It away. I hadn't set my sights high enough, it was plain to see.

Papa put one hand to my shoulder, pulling me back close against him. He wasn't mad anymore. I could tell that right away.

"Girl, it just breaks your poor old Papa's heart," he said. "If you don't have a right sense of your own worth, won't nobody else have it, either. A woman's got to hold herself proud, to my way of thinking. Give It away for a quarter, then you ain't nothing but a two-bit piece of tail. That's the plain and simple truth, as I see it."

"I'm ashamed, Papa," I said, hanging my head. "I'm downright ashamed."

He held me closer. "That's what comes from going out headstrong on your own, without asking the advice of them what knows you and loves you," he said. "I could have told you right from scratch that you were worth a lot more than any old two bits. If you had only thought to ask me."

"I'm sorry, Papa," I said. I *was* sorry, too. It could have been a pile of dollar bills there on the bed, just as easy as anything.

"Then you won't do it no more?"

"I promise," I said, heartfelt. "I promise, Papa. From now on, I'll count myself at my true worth."

"All right. I'm glad to hear it. But just to teach you a lesson you won't forget, I aim to take charge of this change you've accumulated."

"Papa!" I said despairingly.

It wasn't no use, as I well knew; he was already
104

scooping up the money by the double handfuls and pouring it back into the fruit jars. It just broke my heart; made me mad, too, to think of all those long hot afternoons when I had been sharecropping for quarters down there at the artesian well. But there wasn't a thing to be done about it. When Papa made up his mind about something, there wasn't nothing else to be said. I'd never lay eyes again on one cent of all that hard-earned cash.

Done, he straightened to look at me, a different look coming into his face. I realized then that I was naked still, so upset about the money I hadn't taken thought as yet about putting on my clothes.

His two hands went to the buckles of his overalls. He said, "Lay down there on the bed."

I just stared. Here it was still broad open daylight, and he hadn't had the first drink of liquor. Even so, I reckon I wouldn't have had the nerve to deny him if I hadn't been hurt and heartbroken and mad as a wet hen about the money.

"No," I said.

He was still shucking off his overalls. "If any man in the county can have the using of you, I reckon I can, too," he said. "I told you already, I came where you was with nooky on my mind."

I glared at him. "I don't do It without getting paid."

He had his answer to that. Putting his hand into his pocket, he took out a quarter—I reckon it was the same two bits he had saved up during the week to bring to the artesian well—and threw it on the bed. "There. Now lay your ass on George Washington's head and let's get on with It."

I stood without moving. "You just got through telling me it was worth all of a dollar."

I don't know what it was. Maybe it was just that he didn't have a dollar to his name—not counting the quarters in the fruit jars, I mean. Be that as it may, he

105

stared for a long minute, his face showing blacker and blacker; then he turned on his heel and stalked stiff-legged out of the room. I had won.

Of course, when I got dressed and came forth to start supper, I saw that he was sitting out on the front porch in a straight chair tilted back against the wall, staring into nothing and nipping at his jug of piney-woods rotgut. So I knew full well that, come good dark, he'd do his druthers.

Which is how it happened. He ate his supper, not saying word one, and went back to his jug. After washing up the supper dishes, I went to bed and just laid there, not able to go to sleep because I knew he was coming. Then, all of a sudden, he was there in the dark, with that awful smell of liquor on his breath, and I want you to know, he nearly used me up for good that night. It just seemed like he never would quit; every time his nasty old Thing lost it, it found it again right away and started all over, until he got to the point where he couldn't lose it anymore, but couldn't quit either, till I got to feeling like a hundred men had trotted their old Things through my pussy one after the other. When he finally did quit, for the first time I could remember he didn't cry a teardrop—which only showed, I reckon, how things had changed between us. He didn't offer to pay me a thin dime, either.

Next morning at breakfast, he still didn't have nothing to say. Only, when he took his lunch bucket and started for work, he stopped to say, "Remember what you promised me, girl."

"Yes, sir," I said. "I won't forget."

I was just a little bit afraid, when I saw the fellows waiting at the artesian well, about what I had to tell them. My stomach grabbed at itself as I stood thinking: What if they all just laugh out loud and walk off? What then?

But it wouldn't do to go home tonight and tell

106

Papa I had been afraid to ask for a dollar bill instead of a two-bit piece. So I said, keeping my voice as steady as I could, "Fellows, before we get started, I've got to tell you something. From now on, it's going to cost you a dollar apiece."

The lean, mean fellow that always worked me so hard on account of his roughness said, "That's a pretty good raise, ain't it?"

I felt suddenly, I don't know exactly why, just all-fired sure of myself. So I switched my ass at him and said, "If It ain't worth it, then good-bye and farewell." I walked to the camper and climbed in.

I didn't have long to wait. I hadn't taken the time to let them know who was privileged to come first. It was the lean and mean fellow that showed himself in the doorway, a dollar bill in his hand. To tell the truth, though I'm not dead sure about it because I hadn't been able to look them straight in the face whilst I was letting them know about the higher tariff, I don't think a single one quit on me. That's how easy it was.

But I've got to tell you, even with the dollar bills coming in, life wasn't nearly as sweet as it had been. Papa was the reason.

Every day when he came home from work, the first thing he had to know was how much money I had fetched home from the artesian well. Taking the bills in hand, he'd count them one by one, licking his thumb and forefinger between each number. Then he'd wad them up like so much scrap paper, shove them into his pocket, and tell me to fix supper, he was so starved he could eat a boiled bobcat.

Yes, sir. Right then and there, I learned something else about menfolk. They ain't a one of 'em, I don't believe, won't take money offen a woman, given the chance. Oh, he was doing good by me, according to his lights; every day he'd let me keep a dollar for my very own. Now, wasn't that nice of him?

107

So there I was, working harder than ever, and earning my rightful due, too. But no matter how hard I worked, however much I pleased my fellows, I couldn't make myself no more than a dollar a day. I might as well have been picking cotton.

It was not only that Papa was taking and using my money. Every night he'd tackle his liquor jug, and then he'd tackle me. It seemed like, once the dam had let go, he couldn't get enough of his pretty pocket-piece, as he so often called me when feeling loving and tender about his little girl. And Lord, did he ever think of paying *his* dues? You bet your life he didn't.

I put up with it for the longest time because I didn't know what to do about it. But then he got to talking about quiting his job in the pulpwood, which just put my teeth on edge. When he did quit, he spent his days laying around the house in clean overalls picking his teeth and waiting for me to bring home to his greedy pocket my daily earnings.

I put up with it a lot longer then he had any right to expect. After all, he *was* my papa. But the day he started to get suspicious that I was holding out on him, it put the icing on the cake. He'd take the money and count it; then he'd look at me out of the corner of his eyes to say, "Is that all?"

"Yes, sir," I'd say. "Every last dollar."

"Girl, don't lie to me."

"I ain't lying, Papa," I'd say. But all the time I knew he was finding it hard to believe me. When I wasn't telling him nothing but the God's truth.

He couldn't get it out of his mind that I was keeping a few dollars on the sly. But finally he got it worked out how to handle the problem, so he said one day, "I don't see why you have to go traipsing off down there to the artesian well every day, when you could carry on your business right here at home in the finest style." He waited a minute to see if I'd remark to that. I didn't, so he went on. "I'll tell you what. You

108

just let them fellows know they can come on up here
to the house from now on. I'll even lay in some beer
and stuff to enjoy whilst they're waiting their turn."

I just looked at him, this man that had got me into the world. I knew full well what it was he had in
mind. He meant to collect them dollar bills into his
own hand. I'd never even get to touch one.

So I looked at him and I lied in my teeth. "That's
a good idea, Papa. I'll have my own little room, won't
I? It won't be so hot as down there at the artesian
well."

He was so pleased. "I might even put you in an
air-conditioning," he said, smiling. "Soon as I can afford it, anyway. Of course, we'd have to put in the
electric first. So you just tell them they'll be welcome
here any time of the day or night."

"Yes, sir, I thought to myself, and I'll be flat of
my back day and night, whilst you walk around in
clean overalls and count your money.

"Yes, sir," I said. "I'll be sure and tell them."

I went into my bedroom for a minute; then I
took off down the road to the artesian well. I didn't
even look back as I went.

Now, as it happened, there was a very fine fellow there that day named Frank who drove a great
big semi from Florida to New York on a regular run,
hauling citrus. To see me, he only had to swing a
hundred miles or so out of his way. I was pleased to
see Frank, because, like most truckers, he was easy
to get along with, though he couldn't last hardly long
enough to get it in, to tell the dog's truth on him. But
he'd drive all that extra distance to enjoy his half a
minute or so, and was always so nice and kind about
it, too, claiming it wasn't a usual problem but he just
couldn't help thinking about me too hard whilst getting there.

I saved Frank till last. I accepted his dollar, let
him take his shortcut home, and then, while he was

109

putting on his clothes, I said, "Frank, think you could give a girl a ride?"

He was surprised. "Where you going?"

I just smiled and said sweetly, "Why, wherever you're going, Frank."

He couldn't believe his good fortune. His face got all lit up with pleasure, and he put his hands on me, lifting me to my feet and hugging my nakedness.

"God, girl, I didn't know you felt that way about me. I'll show you how to make love, all right. I won't be like I've always been with you. I'll . . ."

I kissed him, but more to hold back his enthusiasm than to encourage it. "We'd better get going, hadn't we?" I said. I laughed. "I'm running away from home, and you sure don't want Papa taking out after you, not if you can help it."

He hustled, then, so in less than a minute we were rolling down the road toward the big highway, me riding shotgun in the roomy, air-conditioned cab of that great big semi, watching Frank push it through all those complicated gears until he had the rig up to speed.

So that was how I come to leave the country where I was born and raised. I wasn't carrying anything with me but the one pretty pair of underpants I owned, made out of nylon instead of flour sacking, because I figured a girl on the road would need at least a change of drawers. It didn't worry my head none that, otherwise, I was leaving empty-handed. I had myself, didn't I? . . . And I had come to know my worth. I felt just as sure as anything that I could make my way in the cold world—at least, as long as some durn-fool man didn't take a notion he was entitled to the dollars I had managed to earn by the sweat of my brow.

By the time it come sundown, we were a good ways along. I reckon Frank was still uneasy about

110

Papa, though, because he kept on driving even after I had remarked two or three times that I was getting pretty hungry and sleepy. It must have been ten o'clock before he pulled into a truck stop for the night.

He maneuvered the semi all the way around to the back. "I'll have to sort of sneak you in," Frank explained. "I'm not sure how the fellow who runs this place might feel about a girl on the premises."

"I was hoping we'd spend the night in a motel," I said. Not ever having done that, I had been counting on it.

He didn't answer to that, just got down on his side and looked carefully around before saying, "Come on. Hurry, now."

We went through the back door into a long corridor, lined on each side with numbered doors. Frank found an empty room, hurried me inside, and closed the door safe behind us.

It was just a tiny room, more like a closet than any place to sleep, the pineboard walls bare except for a girlie calendar that was a couple of years too old to be of use to a mortal soul—I looked at the naked girl, and she didn't have half of what I had got, and was *so* proud of it—and two narrow bunks, one on top of the other, covered with army blankets. There was two thin towels hanging on a wall rack, but no bathroom as far as I could see.

"Where does a body go to the toilet around here?" I asked.

"It's down the hall," he said. "Hot showers and everything."

"Well, I don't aim to go to no bathroom with all these men around," I said. I could hear them laughing and talking far off through the thin walls.

"I'll take care of that problem," Frank said impatiently. He wanted to put his hands on me, I could tell, and he didn't want to think about anything but

111

doing It. "I guess I'd better go check in . . . he'll have seen the rig pull in. You stay right here until I get back . . . won't be more than a minute."

He went away, and I sat down on the lower bunk to wait. He was back in no time, as promised, and I stood up, ready to talk about when and where we were going to eat, when he said, "Now, by God!" and grabbed holt.

Well, when a man's got It on his mind, a girl might as well forget about supper. So I let him have the handling of me, which he did passionately, first feeling me up and then taking off my dress and bra and pants. I giggled and squirmed whilst he did so, which lit his fire just like I thought it would, so that he pushed me down on the hairy blanket, shucked off his breeches like he had found a lighted cigarette in them, and started crawling on top of me.

"What about my dollar?" I said, holding him off with one hand.

"Damn it," he said. "You wanted to run away with me, didn't you? I thought . . ."

"I don't care what you thought," I said. "I get a dollar right on."

Now, that's a man for you. He was so hot and bothered that he didn't know what to do with himself. Still, he wanted to argue about the price.

"But you're *traveling* with me," he said. "I've got you to feed, ain't I, as well as transport? I'm entitled to what I want, when I want It. It's only fair."

"Fair or not fair, I don't do It unless'n I get paid." I swung my legs to put my feet to the floor. "Come on, Frank, let's eat. I'm starving to death."

Angrily he picked up his pants and found a dollar bill. He wadded it up and threw it at me. It hit me on the breast and dropped between my naked legs. But I didn't care; I just picked it up and smoothed it out and said sweetly, "Come on, Frank, show me what you can do."

112

He had bragged beforehand. But, shoot, the min
ute he was astraddle of me, he shoved once and
was done with It. He groaned, laying on me cussing
at himself. I held him tenderly as long as he'd let me.
Which wasn't long.

"That wasn't worth a thin dime," he said bitterly,
sitting up on the side of the bunk.

"Not my fault," I said, as mad now as he had
been before about the money. "I can't help it if you
can't last long enough to let a girl do her thing."

Looking at him then, I softened inside. After all,
he *had* been nice about helping me leave home,
hadn't he? The minute I had let him know I had it in
mind to travel, he had taken me up on it. Besides, I
knew full well that a mean streak in me had made
me giggle and squirm, knowing that when he got too
hot he'd pop like a Chinese firecracker.

So I said, "You lay down there, Frank, let me
do you some good."

The bunk was so cramped, I had to get all the
way out before he could get in. Once he was all set,
I curled myself inside his legs and took his old Thing
in hand, holding up the limpness so I could tickle it
with my tongue. Which perked up interest, let me tell
you. Then I took it gently between my lips, nursing it
nicely, and pretty soon that old Thing was nigh about
as ready as it had ever been.

I got to my knees and told him, "Let me take
care of everything. You just lie there and enjoy It."

Which I did. And he did. Oh, I tell you, I gave
him the best of little old me, just to let him know I
was grateful for the ride. I slipped myself down over
him and moved just as easy and delicate and nice as
a girl can move, and all the time I was watching his
face, so that when he looked like getting too excited,
I'd ease off.

In that way of doing, I held him on the edge for
so long I was driving him up the wall. Finally, of
113

course, he fell over the edge for good and all, and knowing it was now or never, I fucked him to a fare-thee-well, plunging and twisting at the same time, and when he started coming, he didn't know how to stop.

Gone now, all gone and feeling just fine, he reached up with both arms to grab me down on top of him. "Oh, God, girl, oh, God," he kept saying, holding my head with both hands and kissing me all over the face.

"Was it worth the dollar, then?" I whispered into his ear.

"A dollar?" he said. "It was worth a thousand dollars, if a fellow had it. Ten thousand."

Gratified, I kissed him of my own free will; I guess I had showed *him*, hadn't I, not to put a girl down by telling her it wasn't worth a thin dime, when it was all his very own fault?

I got up and started putting on my clothes, telling him, "I don't know about you, but I'm going to get something to eat."

He sat up and reached for his pants. "You can't go up there to the restaurant," he said. "I'll have to bring you a hamburger."

"With french fries and a Coke," I said. "Make it two hamburgers."

He went out. I sat there alone, waiting for him to come back. After a while I decided he must have got hungry, too, being fucked so nice, and was taking a meal before he bothered to fetch my food.

Well, all right, if he wanted to be so selfish-hearted about it; seemed to me like he could have done it the other way around. I waited awhile longer, but then I got to thinking about needing to go to the bathroom. I eased the door open and looked up and down the hallway. Empty. I walked down it, not the way we had come, but the other, and pushed open a door.

114

I was looking for the bathroom, but what I had found was a nice big room all outfitted with couches and chairs and a color television set, which two or three fellows were watching *Bonanza* on, whilst six or seven others were playing blackjack and drinking beer around a big circular table. Just a homey place, it looked like, with nobody but good friends using it.

"Hello, fellows," I said.

The sound of a woman's voice sure did startle them. Even the fellows watching the TV turned around, while at the blackjack table the play stopped entirely.

The dealer, instead of turning the next card, stood up. "Well! Where did *you* come from?"

I laughed. "Frank brought me. You all know Frank, don't you?"

"Yeah, we know Frank," the dealer said. He started to laugh. "Or maybe we just thought we did. I never figured he was all that talented a fellow, to travel with a pretty girl like you."

"It's not that he's traveling with me. I'm traveling with him," I said, laughing at the sharpness of his wit. I do like a witty fellow; it seems like the sharper a man is in his mind, the better he is at doing it. "Can you tell a girl where she can find a bathroom?"

"Right in there," he said, pointing to another door.

"Anybody in there?" I asked. "I ain't accustomed to using the toilet along with the menfolks."

"I don't think so. But I'll see."

He disappeared, to return in a minute with another man. "It's all yours," he assured me.

I went on, and it was just the nicest place you can imagine—four or five wash bowls, with mirrors and lights over them, and three or four johns, each one in its own separateness, and three shower stalls. So I did my business, even to the extent, since I had

115

found a nice dry towel, of taking myself a shower in the hottest water I'd ever enjoyed—I had to bathe out of a washtub at home—and then I combed my hair and put on fresh lipstick.

The minute I appeared, everything stopped in the common room. They every one watched as I walked across the floor. I stopped at the door to look at them again, one by one.

Smiling, I said, "I'm down there in number twelve, in case somebody wants to give a girl a little company."

"What about Frank?" the dealer said.

I frowned. "He left, seems like an hour ago, to get me a hamburger and some french fries. I reckon he must of got lost."

I went on. But I hadn't no more than got in the room and turned around than the dealer was standing in the doorway, a silly grin on his face. I looked at him. He was a nice fellow even with the grin, husky in the shoulders and lean in the hips, though he looked to be nigh about as old as my papa.

"Is It on the house?" he asked, still grinning.

"There ain't nothing on the house around here," I said. "It's going to cost you a dollar."

He didn't hesitate. "All right. Take it off and get in there," and he was already getting naked his own self.

Now, here was a man who knew what a woman's all about. He wasn't in no great big hurry, like so many. No, sir. He took his own sweet time, and in his way he was loving about it, putting his hand between my legs and his mouth on my left nipple and making me feel so warm and good I could have eaten him up with a spoon. These truckers, let me tell you, are something else, though there's a mean one here and there. Which I suppose is true of any bunch of men.

He had me nigh about as interested as he was,

116

even though we were cramped together in that narrow bunk, and when he slid his old Thing into me, I let him know how proud I was to have it there. I do like to see the change in a man's eyes when he first knows what he's let himself in for.

So we started. But Lord, it did come to a screeching halt! All of a sudden there was a bellow of sound, the dealer was snatched up off of me, and another roar of sound as Frank hauled me off the bunk, stood me on my feet, and slapped me halfway across the room.

Which got the dealer mad. He come up fighting and knocked Frank down with one hard lick, then went for him with his boots, which he still had on. Frank grabbed his ankle, twisted him down, and there they were fighting and cussing and just making a terrible racket with the way they rolled around on the floor, thumping and banging against the walls. People were running in the hallway outside, the door slamming open to show their clustered faces.

Didn't nobody make the first move to stop the fight; they just wanted to see it, that was all. I reckon they figured it was a private argument. Some hollered for Frank, but most hollered for the dealer, who seemed to be a popular sort of fellow. Let me tell you, I was on the side of the dealer because of Frank slapping me like that when he didn't have no right. I could feel the bruise on the side of my face, hot and aching and beginning to puff. I sure hoped I wouldn't have a black eye. A girl really looks like she's been into it when she's sporting a black eye.

Frank and the dealer fought it to where they were just wore out with each other. They got to their feet, glaring still but both ready to quit. They were bleeding from scratches and cuts all over their faces. I do believe, though, Frank had got the worst of it.

He was still as mad as a wet hen, glaring at the

117

dealer's nakedness, except for the ankle boots. "By God, I'll cut you down to size, Bob, taking up with a fellow's woman while his back is turned."

"Now, wait a minute," I said. "I ain't nobody's woman."

Frank whirled on me. "You keep your mouth shut. As long as you're traveling with me, what I say goes."

I looked at the fellows crowded in the doorway. I looked at the dealer, Bob. Then I looked at Frank. "Just because I rode in your truck don't mean you own me," I said. "You paid your dollar, and you got your rocks off. That's all I owed you, so I reckon you're paid up in full. And you didn't even bring me my hamburgers and french fries, either."

I looked down on the floor then and saw where he had dropped my supper the minute he had seen Bob on top of me having his good time. All their rolling around on the floor had abused those burgers something terrible.

Frank didn't have nerve enough to answer to the truth I had told him. He looked to the fellows instead, saying, "Get on out of here, all of you. It's between me and her, and I reckon I can take care of her."

Well, I had answer for that. I just smiled at those nice men and said, "I wish you all would run Frank out of my room. I don't aim to get beat up no more." I laughed and wiggled my naked butt. "Besides, maybe some of you lonesome menfolk might want to entertain a girl yourself sometime during the night."

At that, two or three men came on into the room, ready to do my bidding. They got close around Frank, sort of hovering on their toes, one saying, "Damn a man that'll hit a woman, anyway." Frank looked from one to the other, knowing that he had got caught on the short end of the seesaw for sure this time.

Bob started laughing, throwing back his head.

118

Everybody looked at him, he was so happy with his thought.

"Looks like I'm the one ought to stay," he said. "After all, I got some unfinished business to tend to." He turned to me, smiling, his eyes bright on my naked body. "I promise I won't take up much more than an hour of your time."

"Bob has got the dead right of it," I told them. "He was interrupted mighty rudely just when we got to the interesting part."

That's how the scuffle was settled. They hustled Frank out of the room—he didn't like it, but there wasn't much he could do about it—and then all left except Bob. Both still naked, we started in just like it was the very beginning, and I felt so good about him coming to my defense after Frank had slapped me halfway across the room. I just gave him everything I had, and then some more. It was considerably longer than an hour before he left, promising for sure to bring me something to eat.

But I tell you, I couldn't hardly find the time to satisfy my appetite. He had hardly disappeared before the next fellow stood in the doorway, dollar bill in his hand. After that, another. Then a third, before I could catch my breath and sit on the side of the bunk filling myself up with hamburgers and Coke and french fries.

Those truck-driving fellows were just as nice as could be. One brought a hot towel to hold against my cheek, hoping to take out the swelling enough to save me from a black eye. He tended me good, too, coming in between the customers with a towel freshly hotted each time. It was only when he was satisfied he had done the best he could, did he take his rightful turn.

I made twelve whole dollars that night. Which was a pretty good raise for a girl who had left home only today with only one change of underpants. And

119

the next morning I ate breakfast in the common room, fetched for me by the fellows. What a breakfast it was, too! There was pancakes and sausage and three eggs and just lots of butter and maple syrup, and a great big pot of coffee that held at least five cups, though I couldn't drink all of it.

It didn't seem like anybody was anxious to leave on the day's driving, but all sat around talking to me just as friendly as could be. Except Frank. He was sulking at another table, with not a word to say. Hadn't nobody tended *his* bruises, so his face was puffed and raw.

I was taking my time, enjoying myself with my friends, and feeling right to home. Finally Frank said, "For God's sake, come on. I've got to make time today."

I looked at him for the first time. "Where are you headed for, anyway, Frank?"

"New York," he said. "With a load of oranges. You know that."

I looked at the dealer, Bob. "Where you headed for, Bob?"

"Now, wait a minute," Frank said rapidly, standing up. Nobody paid him any mind.

"San Antonio," Bob said. "Running light, to pick up a load of watermelons for Chicago."

"You come here with me, you leave here with me," Frank said.

I shook my head doubtfully. "I don't know. I ain't all that anxious to go all the way up there into Yankeeland." I glanced around. "Where are you all going?"

"Now, by God, I don't aim to have this," Frank said.

Nobody paid him the least mind, but with a sort of walled-up excitement, told me, one after the other. I had my choices, all right, from New York to San Francisco. I looked again to Bob.

120

"I think I'd like to see San Antonio," I said with a slow smile. "Can I ride with you, Bob?"

"Any old time," he said happily. "Ready to roll when you are."

"Now, you don't aim to act mean on me like Frank here did last night?" I warned him.

"Far as I'm concerned, you're a girl in your own right," he said. He grinned. "Just hope you'll keep on taking my dollars, too."

I stood up. "Now, there's a man after my own heart." I looked around. "Hope to see you fellows again somewheres. You've been just as nice as a girl could expect."

Frank had gathered himself up to have his last say. "You come with me, you leave with me," he said. "That's all there is to it."

I looked at him. "I think these friends of mine might have something to say about that."

"You whoring bitch," he said.

"He's getting mean on me again," I complained.

Two or three fellows stood up. Frank looked at them. His eye switched back to me. He was mad, all right. There was hurt in his face I didn't like to see. He had really believed that, out of all the fellows back there at home trying to get me to go somewhere with them, I had picked him.

I guess it don't hurt none for a man to think well of himself. So, going to him, I patted Frank on the cheek. "Frank," I told him, "don't be that way. It may be we'll cross trails again. All you've got to do is have your dollar in your hand. I promise you."

Which somewhat mollified his pride. But still he went on out so he wouldn't have to witness me leaving by my new transportation.

Now, I want you to know that for better than a year I traveled all over America from truck stop to truck stop in those great big semis, and it was just the best time a girl could ever hope to have. Those truck drivers were just the nicest people you could get to know. They'd sneak me into the sleeping quarters, they'd bring me food and anything else I wanted, and all the time I was making money hand over fist; which, for safety's sake, following the advice of a nice older man, I made over into traveler's checks every once in a while. Because I didn't have hardly any expenses to speak of, my purse got more and more stuffed with those little books of safety checks, to the point where I got to feeling right down rich.

I'll always have a soft spot in my heart for a cross-country truck driver, because they were good people to have on your side. Oh, I'd run into a meanie every once in a while, or a strange fellow that liked to do strange things, or have strange things done to him—there's more men like that in the world than a girl could imagine if she didn't know better—but always the others around were willing and able to protect me from anything real bad.

And, oh, they just did me proud. And the adventures we did have! There was the time, for instance, when a whole bunch of us got snowed in up in Colorado by a sudden April blizzard. Fifteen fellows and me. They set me up in the prettiest motel suite you ever saw, just down the road from the truck stop where they were all staying, and I had the thickest towels and the hottest water and the best food—I ate in the motel restaurant, just like a lady, and of course by this time I had nice clothes and everything—and then they'd come to see me in the night, one by one, to do It with me.

Such traveling lasted more than a year, as I said —a good time I won't soon forget. It was during this time I truly learned my trade and set my rules. I wouldn't travel with any one fellow more than a few days at a time; and always, if they didn't know already—of course, I was getting to be famous nationwide, by word of mouth, and after a while nearly everybody understood how I was—I let them know right in front what they could expect and what they couldn't.

I wouldn't take on anybody who had liquor on his breath. They had to be stone-cold sober to come to me with a hot dollar in their hand. I didn't ever tell nobody why, but it was that if I smelled liquor, I couldn't help but feel like it was Papa with his thick old Thing inside of me; and there had always been something about that I just couldn't like. I reckon it was because he was the only man I had ever done It with that didn't pay me my due.

A real good life. I had my little suitcase to carry nice changes of clothes, just the one piece of luggage and my purse, so I could travel light and ready. After I had money ahead, once in a month or so I'd lay over for a couple of days in a nice motel, all by myself, during which time I'd see two movies every day, or just lay around and watch television and soak in the bathtub. But pretty soon I'd get lonesome for my friends, so I'd show up at the nearest truck stop looking for the next ride. They were always *so* glad to see me.

So it went until I come to my first great city, New Orleans, Louisiana. If I had known how life was going to change on me, I never would have set foot across that city line.

Or, taking the good and the bad, maybe I would have. I don't know.

The Boy

For the first time in my life, I was at loose ends with myself. It was a strange sort of feeling. It was not only there didn't seem to be nothing to do; I didn't *want* to do anything. Now that there wasn't no purpose in going back to Charlotte Ainsley's house, there wasn't any reason to anything.

Even worse, for the first time I could remember, Billy didn't seem to be with me anymore. It was only after he was gone—of course, he had been *gone* for a long time now, because he died of a fever when me and him were nine years old—that I realized just how much I had counted on him being there, somewhere just behind my left shoulder. In my mind, you see, I was always checking with Billy. What would Billy do? Or what would Billy think? Or what would Billy feel? About this, that, or the other thing. Most important of all, as I passed through a day of life, what would Billy *see* in that day, take note of, appreciate,

124

and enjoy? I had got so used to living life twice over, once for Billy and once for me.

For a week or more I moped around the house, getting up early in the morning only to look at all that empty time up ahead before I could rightfully sleep again. I didn't go swimming, I didn't go sailing, I didn't go downtown to shoot a game of pool.

I didn't want to work. Mr. Adams found out I was idle, so he called two or three times, trying to persuade me to take up the grocery route. But even when he offered me one raise after the other, I couldn't take interest anymore in that line of work.

Which was just about the strangest part of it all. Because I did like my old ladies. I enjoyed doing for them. Not on account of the tips and the nice presents, either, but because it's just a good feeling to be appreciated in this world. And they did appreciate me.

It wasn't that I didn't have my chances. Hardly a day went by that I didn't get a phone call asking me to mow a yard or weed a garden. I told all these good friends of mine that, feeling under the weather as I did, I couldn't see my way clear to take on a job of work just at this time. I tried to be nice about it. But I wouldn't see them.

It seemed like that Charlotte Ainsley, in doing her great piece, had used up the best part of me. She had burned me right down to the ashes, and all I had to show for it was the gold chain. I had that, at least; and I never took it off, except to take a shower, and I had got into the habit of fingering and feeling its heavy links as they hung down on my chest.

Not that I felt *bad* about what Miss Charlotte had done. I felt fine about it. Every time the thought crossed my mind of that statue being gazed on by thousands of people, it just made me feel great all over. The best part was, I knew that it would live forever, regardless of what happened to me. I would get

125

old—why, I'd be thirty before you knew it—but the statue couldn't get old. It would always and forever be sixteen, standing at full tilt and more alive than me.

I was empty. The magic that had been a part of me—it *had* been magic, too, for it seemed like any old lady in the need couldn't take but one look at me without falling under its spell—had been transferred to the statue. So in one way Miss Charlotte's statue had given me immortality, in another it had taken it away, leaving me a mortal man. No more to me than any other man.

The magic might now dwell in the statue; but it could still have its effect on my life. Because it was Charlotte Ainsley's statue that brought Miss Ruby to me.

Two o'clock of a Thursday afternoon, hot and still. Out in the Gulf a thunderhead was building itself from the heat, towering there white and tall like a dream castle made out of hot air. No wind, so the sailboat or two I could see looked like they had been painted on the water. Just then, while I had been thinking for ten minutes I ought to go into the house and get a drink of water, a limousine pulled up to the gate. It was the longest and the prettiest automobile I had ever seen, sporting a special paint job of deep purple. Though I hadn't ever seen one before, I knew from the hood ornament that it was a Rolls-Royce.

A tall fellow, old and settled-looking in his ways, though wearing a purple uniform to match the car, got down and came through the front gate that hadn't been fixed for a good many years now, and so sagged on one hinge. He picked his way through the chicken droppings in the bare sand of the yard and stopped at the porch steps. Nobody around but me; my younger brothers and sisters down off in the willow thicket playing, Daddy downtown to enjoy the cool of the poolroom, Mama taking a nap in the back bedroom, which was the coolest place in the house.

126

He didn't have any doubt that I was the man he had come to see, because, politely taking off his cap, he said, "Miss Ruby wants to see you."

Like always these days, I was disinclined to go anywhere, do anything. "Who's Miss Ruby, and where is she?" I asked.

"Miss Ruby is Miss Ruby," he said. Then, nodding his head, "She's in the car, waiting to talk to you."

Having no desire to seem impolite, I figured I could bestir my laziness enough to walk that far. So I went out to the purple limousine, the chauffeur fellow following. When we got there, I still couldn't see anything, because the back seat was shaded with window blinds. The chauffeur fellow moved around in front of me and opened the door.

"Get in here, boy, and let me have a look at you," a deep, rough voice said.

I got in. The chauffeur fellow had left the motor running, so the air-conditioning had it nice and cool.

Miss Ruby was a woman big enough to match the size and the deepness of her voice. Not that she was fat, though there was aplenty of that; just *big*, that's all, her shoulders broad, her thighs like the twin boles of oak trees, and she had the chest of a pouter pigeon. Big hands, salted with flashing rings, and a broad face, pale in color, as though she didn't ever let the sun get to her, and a tiny rosebud mouth that was as sweet and kind as her black eyes were sharp.

The automobile started moving. I said, "Wait a minute. I can't be going nowhere."

She didn't pay me any mind; she was busy opening up a bar built into the back seat there, and putting ice into a silver cup.

"Want a shot of sour mash, son?" she asked, glancing at me.

"No, ma'am, I don't drink," I said politely.

She tossed back the shot and smacked her lips.

127

"Better learn to drink, boy. At my age, sour mash is damn nigh as good as sex, and twice as handy." She chuckled at her own saying, so I laughed too.

"How old are you, my boy?" she asked in a friendly tone.

"Eighteen," I said, like I always did.

She kept on looking. "You're a liar. Not a day over sixteen, and you know it."

Well, now, how did she know that?

"Maybe you're wondering why I'm here," Miss Ruby said.

"Yes'm," I said politely. "I reckon I am."

She fixed herself another shot of sour mash and tossed it back neat, just one ice cube in the silver cup. Then she closed up the bar and sat back to study me.

"It just happened that I drove over today to visit an old friend, son," she said. "Knew Charlotte Ainsley years ago in London, when she was first making her reputation." Her whole body shook with laughter. "That was before she went les, I want you to understand. In fact, I didn't know she had gone that route until I took note of that pretty girl she's got living with her."

She stopped, smacked her lips in remembrance of the taste of Jack Daniel's, and went on.

"Saw that newest thing she's done. Liked it. Tried to buy it. She wouldn't hear of selling it, even to an old friend with the right size of money. Swore she couldn't let it go except into a great museum, which she was sure it would do after her New York show this winter." Miss Ruby's chest shook with laughter. "Invited me to make the donation to a museum of her choice, but I don't have a charitable bone in my body." She stopped laughing as suddenly as she had started. "She's right, of course. It's a museum piece of the first water, if you don't mind my saying so." She chuckled all over herself again.

128

The limousine was creeping along slowly. We might as well have been in a private living room; the panel was closed between us and the driver, the window shades were drawn, the interior lit by soft, hidden lights. There was music playing somewhere, soft and easy, just on the edge of hearing. Some automobile, all right; you couldn't hardly tell that it was moving.

"Since I couldn't own the work of art, I thought I'd have a look at the original. For some reason or other, Charlotte tried to keep you a secret. But I got it out of her finally, and since I'm a lady who makes up her mind in a hurry, I drove right over here."

I didn't say anything. There wasn't much to be said about all that she had told me.

Miss Ruby was still looking at me. "Did you like what she had done, once it was finished?"

"Yes'm," I said. "I liked it a whole lot."

"Well, boy, I'm here to view the original," she said. "So flop it out here and let me see it."

I didn't move. She waited for an instant; then she reached over, squirming around in her seat, to unzip my pants. Her large hand plunged in and dragged Him out. You would have thought such attentions would stir His interest, but they didn't. She began to manipulate Him.

"Are you always this slow, boy?" she said.

I put one hand to the gold chain to feel its heavy links. "No'm, I reckon not," I said. "I just ain't been feeling any too well lately."

Her sharp eyes studied my face all over again. "Well, we'll just see about that," she said strongly.

I must tell you, she had a kindly hand, and you know how He's got a mind of His own. Before I hardly realized it, willy-nilly there He was, all of Himself.

Miss Ruby gazed upon Him. "I'll be damned," she said. "I'd have bet a hundred dollars she improved

Him some, though Charlotte swore not. She was, by God, telling the straight truth, wasn't she?"

Letting Him stand by his lonesome, she started rummaging around on the rear-window ledge and finally produced the last free-standing model Miss Charlotte had made. She held the clay model on my leg beside Him, nodding in approval.

"Absolutely," she said. "That's a fine cock you've got there, boy." She looked into my face, laughing at my expression. "I bought all her working models, son, talked her into letting me have those, at least. Two hundred dollars each. But I've got an idea exactly what to do with them."

It hurt me to know that Miss Charlotte had sold even the working models. I comforted myself by thinking that they had, at least, fallen into hands that would appreciate their quality.

Miss Ruby put away the model. "How'd you like to work for me, son?"

I shook my head. "Like I told you. I ain't been feeling so good lately."

"Anything *physically* wrong?"

I started fingering the chain again. "No'm. Not that I know of."

"Are you working now?"

"Ain't doing nothing but sitting."

"Know anything about boats?"

I showed a spark of interest for the first time. "I've sailed a good bit, like any other boy raised in Pass Robin."

She nodded. "That's just fine. Son, let me tell you something. That artist woman has wrung you dry, that's all there is to it. But it's time you got up off your ass and started living again. You won't feel any better until you do."

I didn't say anything. But I was listening to her deep, rough, kindly voice.

"You've got something, boy, and it'd be a damned
130

shame to let it go to waste. Now, working on a boat ought to be just the ticket. Especially the *Liberated Lady*." She put her hand on my bare arm, stroking it down. Her big hand was surprisingly soft, surprisingly gentle. "You'd be gorgeous with a real tan, the good deep kind you can get only from living on a boat. My crew work naked most of the time, once we're well out from port where no one can bother us."

"You mean you've got a whole crew?" I said.

She chuckled. "She's a big boat, seventy-five feet. Plenty of room for anything you might want to do." She paused. "It's a good life, son. The kind of life you need right now."

I thought about it. It sounded good.

"Where is this boat?"

"I sail out of New Orleans."

It sounded even better. I knew suddenly that I needed to get out of Pass Robin. Hadn't thought about it until this minute. But I knew.

"All right," I said, so quick it surprised me. "You've hired yourself a hand, Miss Ruby."

"Now, just one minute," she said, laughing and holding up one hand. "Got to try you out first. Never hire a new hand without testing him."

"All I know is sailboats," I said. "But I . . ."

She wasn't listening. Instead, she had picked up the voice tube and was saying to the chauffeur fellow up front, "Paul, that Holiday Inn we passed on the way in . . . stop there, please." She cut an eye at me and added, "We might even stay the night, so book a nice suite."

She hung up the voice tube, put her hand on Him again. I understood, by now, that it wasn't anything like an examination for a mate's license that I had to pass.

It was a luxurious suite, king-size bed and everything. Paul brought in a couple of suitcases—I learned later she never traveled without being ready to stop

131

anywhere, for as long as she liked—and then proceeded to replace the motel sheets with purple-silk sheets. Gathering up the towels, he put thick purple towels in their place. Then he went away.

While Paul had been doing his work, Miss Ruby and I had sat in two chairs watching him. I felt sort of strange in all this elegance, wearing a sleeveless shirt—I had just torn the sleeves out, leaving it ragged —and a pair of khaki pants. I didn't even have any shoes.

Miss Ruby heaved herself to her feet—standing, she was taller than me, and broader too, just the biggest woman I'd ever seen—and went to the bar Paul had fetched from the limousine.

Pouring herself a drink and knocking it back, she said without looking at me. "Strip off."

I did. But I moved mighty slow about it, and didn't have much to show when I stood naked. Miss Ruby turned around, after her second shot of sour mash, and gazed at me with a curious expression, like she didn't know whether to laugh or to cry.

She didn't say anything, just got busy taking off her own clothes. Which was quite a job. She was wearing this long purple gown, all the way to her ankles, and under it there was this girdle. Finally, tugging and heaving under the gown, she shucked herself out of the girdle, flinging it aside with a great sigh of relief.

"I hate that thing," she said. "Don't know why I wear it. But a woman's got to have some pride, I reckon. Come here and unbutton me."

The gown was fastened with a long row of buttons down the back. I was pretty much fumble-fingers, because I wasn't all that anxious to gaze upon her huge nakedness. Getting impatient before I had worked halfway down her back, she stripped off the gown over her head, regardless of her careful hairdo.

132

"Come on," she said. "Get on the bed."

"Miss Ruby," I said.

She turned sharply. "What's the matter?"

"I don't think I can do it."

She looked at Him. "Boy, you're mighty young to have that kind of trouble."

I had my hand to the gold chain, the heaviness of the links so comforting. "It's not that," I told her. "It's just that . . . I ain't used to having to prove nothing."

Her eyes rose to my face. "Listen, son, I've got to try you out before I hire you. But don't think for a minute that a big fat ugly woman like me doesn't need to get her ashes hauled, just the same as your pretty young things. Just looking at that thing, limp as it is, makes me feel like warm Jell-O inside."

I couldn't answer to that.

Her gruff voice got deeper and softer. "It's all to do with Charlotte Ainsley, isn't it?"

"Yes'm," I said uneasily. "I reckon so."

Her face turned soft, her rosebud mouth just as pretty as the mouth on any girl. "Come lie with me," she said. "You don't have to do a thing. I just want to hold you, that's all."

We laid down together on the king-size bed. Miss Ruby laid her arms around my waist, holding me close, stroking with her strong and gentle hands. It was not that she was trying to rouse me to my duty; just tender loving and a heartfelt care for the down feeling that dwelled so deeply in my soul.

I laid my head on her broad shoulder. I put one hand on her breast, breathing deeply to take in the musky perfume she was wearing. That was a thing that Billy would have done; and suddenly Billy was with me again, breathing that scent just like I was. And so we laid together, the three of us, her and me and Billy, for the longest time, the air-conditioning

133

whispering in the silent room. I took pleasure in the silk sheets, for I had never laid down my body on such fine sheets before.

At long last she spoke quietly. "You let that lesbian artist cut you down pretty good, didn't you?"

"It wasn't that," I said. "I liked Charlotte fine. It's just that . . ."

"Just that what?"

Held so lovingly, feeling the warm closeness of Miss Ruby's great body, I could say it. To myself, as well as to her.

"It's just that . . . I keep knowing myself a mortal man."

Her massive arms held me more tightly. "Of course you're mortal. But you're a man, son. A real man. That's what counts."

I hesitated over the words. "But the piece of work that Charlotte made out of Him . . ."

"You wanted her to make it, didn't you?"

"I sure did. But . . ."

"Listen," Miss Ruby said. "You believe that piece of clay took it all, don't you? You must remember that you're a man, while it's only a piece of clay. A great work of art, no doubt about that . . . no real woman will ever be able to look upon it without feeling a tenderness and a wanting down in her gut. That's a mighty thing, all right. But . . ."

She raised up on her elbow to gaze into my face. "But that piece of clay can't *fuck* a woman, son. Can't go up in there to stir her up, make her know herself for all the woman she's capable of being. You can. So you're a mighty work of art yourself—just because you *are* so fragile, like a butterfly in your youth, you are human and you are mortal and you will not last forever."

I didn't say anything. She leaned to kiss me, and still she wasn't trying to rouse me. A kindly kiss.

"Do you understand?"

"I'm trying to."

I didn't understand. But I had a feeling that Billy did, and Billy was with me again, and so that feeling was enough.

Miss Ruby lifted the weight of the gold chain in her hand. "Charlotte Ainsley gave you this, didn't she?"

I wondered how she knew. "Yes," I said. "When we had finished the work we had to do together."

"Take it off," Miss Ruby said.

"I don't have to," I said.

I rolled myself up and onto her, feeling her great legs part to let me sink into my place on her body. I took Him in hand, limp though He was, and put Him into her pussy. Then I just laid there and let Him grow to his natural size and heft, pushing at her warm flesh inch by inch, making His way into her. When I cocked my hips for the first stroke, she let out a long sigh, so that now it was me stroking her, comforting her, whilst she laid open under me, all that great size and all that great loving.

There came, then, the moment when it changed, when fucking Miss Ruby got to be like riding a hurricane wave on a skateboard. She just suddenly warped into it, such a big woman, and so passionate, all I could do was hang on, and the funny thing was, this big woman was small and tight inside, so I just filled her to the hilt.

Socketed home now, she started coming to me, and one thing led to another, the big waves shuddering up from deeper and deeper inside her, each wilder than the one before, until I just went crazy my own self, so that we rode together into the eye of the storm, where it was so quiet and peaceful you couldn't believe it.

Still wrapped in each other, we slept for a time, then did it all over again, just like it hadn't happened yet. After which, she picked up the telephone to order room service, steak and mashed potatoes and a great big salad for each of us. We ate, and did it again, then we slept some more and woke up in the dawn's early light to put on the finishing round.

It's hard to believe, but instead of getting satisfied, she grew more passionate with each trial. I had thought the first time was wild enough; but that last early-morning round, when she got up on her hands and knees, with Him into her from behind, I was afraid she was going to tear the bed down.

Over room-service breakfast, a double order of pancakes for both, she said sweetly, "Son, you're a fucking genius. *And* got the equipment to match."

"It's just that I've been without," I said modestly. Which was true. I hadn't touched me a woman for more than a week.

She snorted in disbelief. "In fact, I intend to pay you twice what I'm paying the other boys." She shook a warning finger. "But don't let them know."

"Regular wages is fine with me," I said.

"You're worth it." She looked steadily into my eyes. "That is, if you're prepared to go to work for me."

"Yes'm, Miss Ruby," I said. "You're just the finest lady I've ever run across. I *want* to work for you."

That was how, for the first time in my life, I left Pass Robin and set out into the world to make my way.

It didn't take but the first boat ride to find out what the *Liberated Lady* was all about. It wasn't sailing, let me tell you that.

She was a beautiful thing, all teakwood and shining brass, with great big Chrysler engines. There was a lounge topside, glassed in all around, with tables and chairs and a bar and all, and down below, a galley all shining and clean, and four staterooms. Miss Ruby's stateroom was a gorgeous place for a great woman, all purple, with a queen-size bed that took up nearly all the space.

136

The captain of the *Liberated Lady* was a weathered old woman, half the size of Miss Ruby but twice as loud, who was ugly as a mud fence in her seagoing breeches, made out of canvas, and her battered captain's hat. But she, by God, knew how to run a boat.

The crew was me and three other boys, each in his own way a fine-looking fellow and proud of himself. They all three had those deep tans Miss Ruby kept talking about. I don't aim to go into any detailed descriptions of the crewmen, because they kept changing all the time I was with Miss Ruby. In fact, one quit the day after I came aboard because Miss Ruby called me to her stateroom instead of him. He took it sort of personal, because Friday night had always been his, and he had come to count on it.

But, shoot, there wasn't enough seamanship to working on the *Liberated Lady* to put in your hat, except for keeping the brasswork shining and the teak decks polished, which we did whilst docked in the marina. And here's why, as I come to find out. On the Saturday, along about three o'clock in the afternoon, I noticed that Captain Phoebe was getting ready to put to sea. Then, in about half an hour, here come a bevy of ladies, arriving all excited and flustery in taxis or private cars, flocking aboard until there was a dozen of them, all told. Me and the other crew members—only three of us, now that one had left this morning—were leaning over the rail, watching the activity.

We were all dressed alike, in a sort of uniform, if what we wore could be called a uniform. It wasn't nothing in the world but a sort of black bikini that didn't cover up hardly nothing. I felt awkward and embarrassed being so undressed out there in public like that. The other fellows seemed well used to it, so I reckoned I could stand it too, given time.

"Here they come, the horny old biddies," said the crewman that had a sort of mean streak to him.

137

(He didn't last long after I got there; Miss Ruby threw him off the boat for beating up on a lady one time.)

"Now, there's one I wouldn't mind taking advantage of," the redheaded fellow said.

He raised an arm and waved. So many of the women waved back, I couldn't tell which one he was talking about.

I had my own thoughts, by now, what the *Liberated Lady* was all about. But those ladies coming aboard sure didn't look like they could be all that hard up. Most were pretty young, and even the older ones were just as nice as they could be. Only two or three out of the whole bunch that a fellow couldn't be anxious to get into bed with, and be proud of the chance.

For they were classy ladies every one, wearing beautiful clothes just exactly right for a seagoing adventure. You could tell money lay heavy in their backgrounds, because they had the look of ladies who went to the best hairdressers, whose bodies knew only expensive clothes, and all. There's a way a woman walks who's been raised rich like that; you can just tell at a glance that they are somebody.

We cast off and headed out toward Chandeleur Island. Once well away from the land, one of the fellows said, "Well, guys, let's give the girls a thrill," and shucked out of his bikini.

The other crewmen followed suit. And, hell, I've got to tell the truth, I didn't see nothing remarkable between their legs.

The fellow with the mean streak turned to me. "Bashful, boy?" he said, leering. "Or are you afraid to show what you got?"

Now, I wasn't all that used to undressing in front of other men. But, seeing no reason to be ashamed of myself, I stripped off the bikini and flung it to one side.

138

They stood silent. Finally, the redheaded fellow whistled. "Boy! Where did Miss Ruby find *that?*"

But, hellfire, do you think those ladies were out there cheering and carrying on over our nakedness? Don't bet your life on it. As I quickly found out, they had already chose up partners and had three tables of bridge going in the lounge. From the expressions on their faces, so tight and grim, and the lack of social conversation—as I saw when I strolled past the windows to find out exactly what was going on —they weren't playing for peanuts, neither.

So it's gambling, I told myself. *That's* what the *Liberated Lady* is all about. Which relieved my mind, because even if we split them up between us, it wouldn't be the right thing to do to take care of the needs of four ladies one right after the other. At least, not in my book, because I ain't no stud, and never claimed to be one.

This was the way it worked. Captain Phoebe just took the *Liberated Lady* out to anchor for the night. Early in the morning we'd come back in again; and that's all the seamanship we ever had to deal with. The least patch of rough weather, we'd up an-. chor and come on in, because you take a lady that's sick to her stomach, she ain't going to take much interest in gambling.

A bridge-playing cruise, like this one, was a sort of kindergarten class. Only taking a house cut from each table, Miss Ruby actually lost money on bridge cruises. But when she spotted a lady with the right spirit, Miss Ruby would invite her confidentially to come along for the *real* action, which was blackjack or a roulette wheel, whichever Miss Ruby felt like running that particular night. She dealt her own blackjack and ran her own wheel, and I tell you, she was something to see sitting there in her purple gown —she never wore anything but purple—her big clever hands dealing the cards or twirling the wheel, and

139

taking in and pushing out chips like they had a life of their own. The smallest chip stood for a hundred dollars. Those ladies were dyed-in-the-wool gamblers; when real gambling was going on, the crewmen might just as well have been so many alligators wallowing around on deck, unless a lady happened to bust out and decided to console herself with another kind of action. This one nice lady, every time she lost all her money, she'd take us all on, one right after the other. She always seemed to lose so quick, I wondered, sometimes, if maybe it just wasn't her way of paying her dues to give herself a rightful shot at us boys.

The bridge was for pretty high stakes, too, just to break them in right. And Miss Ruby had her own little ways of making a bridge cruise right interesting, because she wanted the ladies all stirred up and feeling risky. Only then could she find out which were the high-rollers, and which weren't.

The bridge games had gone on all afternoon. As it came sundown, Miss Ruby broke out the liquor so the ladies could partake of a social hour. The crewmen hadn't ventured inside the lounge, but stayed out on deck, getting our full tans. Miss Ruby fed the ladies—that's when I found out there was a cook in the galley, and a steward to serve—and afterward another round of drinks, mostly fancy stuff this time, or a snifter of brandy.

Miss Ruby came to find me. "It's time I showed you to the ladies," she said. "Come along."

I didn't know what was about to happen, but, buck naked as I was, I followed. Miss Ruby shielded me from direct view by standing in front of me whilst she called them to attention by rapping a spoon against a glass.

"Ladies, I want to show you our door prize for tonight," she said. "So pay attention now."

They got quiet. I was still hidden behind her bulk—at least, pretty much so.

140

"Remember the lovely new pieces of art I picked up this week?" she said. She gave her hearty laugh. "I must say, each and every one showed proper appreciation."

I saw, then, that on each bridge table, as a centerpiece, was one of Charlotte's models of Him. So that was why, as they were settling down to begin, there had been so much laughing and carrying on.

"Now I have a secret to reveal. I've found the original of those models," Miss Ruby said in her deep, laughing voice. "And here he is, our newest crew member . . . if you'll pardon the expression."

With that, she stepped to one side, to show me standing there.

Not a sound in the room. The ladies looked at me, while I looked at them. And I want you to know, their eyes were so bright, their silence so appreciative, it stirred Him, so that He started coming to a stand. It seemed like an hour, though it was only a minute or two, at best, while those nice ladies watched Him rise slowly to his proudest.

"Now, that's what I call a door prize," Miss Ruby said. "And one of you lucky ladies shall win this lovely specimen for her very own. At midnight, a drawing will be held. The winner can reserve this grand cock for her private pleasure; or, if she so desires, she can auction Him off to the highest bidder."

I want you to know, that stirred them up. A murmur of sound whispered through the lounge, along with a nervous laugh or two; and one lady, covering her eyes with her hands, blushed a bright red, blurting out, "Oh, I just came along to play bridge!" Which brought a general laugh.

Miss Ruby turned to me. "Pass among them and give each a ticket." Which I did, Miss Ruby singing out, "No touching now, ladies, please, you'll have to wait till midnight, just like Cinderella," which

141

made everybody laugh a lot more than the joke counted for.

As I went among them, handing each a numbered ticket, some looked at Him and some didn't; one lady, I couldn't tell which, because she did it from behind, sneaked her warm hand against the bend of my knee, then moved it up under my ass to barely touch my balls. Which caused Him to jerk and tighten. Didn't see which lady; just knew she wore a lot of rings.

The minute I was through, I left the lounge, motioning secretly for Miss Ruby to follow. Out on deck, I said, "Miss Ruby, I think you've got me wrong. I ain't no stud. I ain't never done it on account of money, and I never will."

Miss Ruby took me as serious as I had meant the words. "Son, you're working for me, not the lady who's lucky enough to win the draw. Then . . . it's between you and her. But *she's* not paying you. I am."

"It seems like kind of a narrow line to draw, don't it?" I said dubiously.

She put her strong hand on my arm. "You've always had heart for a needful woman, haven't you?"

"Yes'm, I reckon so," I said. "But . . ."

"But nothing. Do you think *any* of these women would have accepted an invitation to cruise on the *Liberated Lady* if they hadn't needed *something* to brighten up their lives? They all knew in front, more or less, what was going down. So if the lady who draws you doesn't happen to want you, she has the privilege of auctioning you off to somebody who does. The lady gets the auction money, not you . . . and some of these gambling women, they'd rather have cold cash than a warm cock any day of the week. Especially if they've been losing." She squeezed my arm. She gave me her sweet smile. "Just remember, son. You're doing it for me."

142

I stood thinking about it. Then I looked her straight in the eye. "I aim to keep the right to turn down anybody I feel like turning down."

It shook Miss Ruby. But then she nodded in agreement. "All right. If that's the way you want it, I'll let them know before the drawing takes place. In that case, the lady who wins the draw, or tops the auction, will have her choice of one of the other fellows."

I felt relieved. "That's fine with me."

She patted my arm. "I admire you for your principles. So will the lady; take my word for it."

I went up to sit in the bow for a while by myself. The more I thought about it, the shrewder I realized Miss Ruby was. If she had shown the door prize during the afternoon, whilst they had their minds on the game, it would have gone down wrong for sure. But after they'd had their drinks, and their dinner, and then some more drinks, everybody relaxed from the high-stakes gambling, just the very idea of such daringness put a thrill into them they couldn't deny.

Now, I had always had the idea that ladies liked above all to be private in their doings—though I had known some who just had to brag about Him to a good friend. But, being in it all together aboard the *Liberated Lady*, it just sort of let them cut loose, so they were not only not afraid to let their desires show, they were actually egging each other on, daring any one of them to show herself less free and easy in the situation. After all, nothing that happened on the *Liberated Lady* counted in their everyday life; it was all great fun and deep games, a spice to the lure of gambling. And so I learned something about womenfolks I hadn't known before; this waiting for the big event of the door prize made the bidding and the play of the hands heavier and riskier, their laughter was sharper, their faces were flushed, their eyes were brighter. There wasn't a one of them but didn't want the greater risk of winning Him.

143

When eleven o'clock rolled around, Miss Ruby stopped the tournament and invited the ladies on deck for drinks and dancing. Me and the other crewmen, dressed now in white trousers and dark-blue blazers, for it would have been indecent to dance naked with the ladies, danced in turn with each guest. Some couldn't wait their turn, so chose up dancing partners amongst themselves, to much kidding, of course, by all the others.

There was a bright moon, full, making it just beautiful out there on the still water, with the soft, celestial music wafting us about the deck. I just knew that Billy would have appreciated the scene. Of course, I wasn't much of a dancer, but, shoot, they just wanted to lay their bodies close and feel Him through the cloth of my pants. A couple of the ladies got bold enough, with the drinks and the music and the moonlight, to whisper that it would be the luckiest night of their lives if they happened to win His favor.

By the time midnight come around, and I made the draw out of a bar bucket, I had begun to feel appreciated all over again, so that I knew that, whoever won, I wouldn't want to deny them their reward. Which was a good thing, because the lady who won me—the young, pretty thing who had blushed and covered her face at the very idea— didn't know exactly how to take advantage of her good fortune.

"Oh, Lord!" she said helplessly. "What do I do now?"

Which made the other ladies laugh, let me tell you, and call out, "Auction, auction!" and "Highest bidder!" She blushed all the rosier, though, as I noticed, she couldn't take her eyes off of me, which made me to think she liked the idea of winning, but couldn't bring herself close to admitting it in such public fashion as the situation demanded.

"It all depends on whether you like money more, Mary," Miss Ruby said in her loud, tough voice. "Remember, it's your choice."

Standing there in my nice white pants and blue blazer, I was wishing Mary would just take me by the hand and claim Him. It was not only that I figured she could use a sample of what He had in store; I didn't relish the idea of being sold to the highest bidder. It might just curl Him up, sensitive as He was, if He didn't fetch a good price. Of course, I reminded Him, we were her property to do with as she would, so it wasn't my place to say anything. So I smiled at her and waited. But I did touch her secretly on the back, with the fingertips of one hand.

Which flustered her even more, if that was possible. She just couldn't admit it to herself, so she jerked away from my hand and said, "I suppose I should put Him up for auction, I really should."

Everybody laughed again, which only firmed up her intention. "Yes," she said. "I think I'll do just that." She got a stubborn look to her face. "I'll conduct the auction myself."

"Honey, you just go right ahead," Miss Ruby said. "It's your show."

Having made the decision, she turned bold as brass. Her eyes flashed to me. "You'll have to allow the ladies to view the merchandise, dear."

"You heard the boss, son," Miss Ruby said. "Go down and take off those nice clothes. Then come to the lounge."

Going below, I did as told. When I returned, Miss Ruby had taken advantage of the delay to move the ladies into the lounge and get a fresh drink into everybody's hand. She was doing everything she could to make the affair a success. And succeeding.

So I walked naked into a situation that, with the feeling of sex and excitement heavy in the air, brought Him instantly to a fine, hard stand. The la-

145

dies applauded, their eyes bright and ready, at the
sight of Him, as my owner took me by the hand and
led me to the chair I was to stand on. Given the no-
holds-barred atmosphere Miss Ruby had created so
cleverly, they could all act out their desires like
never before in their lives. Women are much more
that way than men, I do believe, once given the
opportunity to let go all holds and be their true
selves. As long as it don't count.

"Are you *sure* you want to offer that to the
highest bidder?" someone called.

It was greeted with more laughter than you
could imagine. My owner blushed again. "Well, I intend to place a reserve of fifty dollars," she said.
They all just hollered, making her explain breath-
lessly, "Because that's how much I've lost tonight."

Then, forcing herself to a brave, free gesture, she
motioned for me to give her the gold chain around my
neck, which she then proceeded to drape on Him.
The weight of the gold links bowed his head, but
not enough so the chain slipped off.

"Here he is, ladies, the finest stud in the land,
all yours for the money. Do I hear fifty dollars?"

I wanted to tell her I wasn't no stud, but I
didn't. Mostly, I think, because I was suddenly wondering if anybody meant to bid after all. Because
didn't nobody say nothing.

My owner, really getting into the action, stroked
my hip with her hand, then reached to cradle my
balls. I could feel her fingers trembling. "Fifty dollars
for this fine cock, ladies, now don't be bashful, let's
hear fifty dollars!"

"Hell, I'll take Him myself at that price," Miss
Ruby said with a deep laugh. "Fifty dollars!"

"Sixty!" somebody sang out, and someone else,
"Seventy-five!" and it was rolling.

A weird feeling it was, let me tell you, to see

146

how those old ladies took the spirit of the occasion. I don't reckon a single one but didn't get in one bid, at least, just to prove to herself she hadn't laid back shy. The price went up and up, jumping ten and twenty dollars at a crack. But at last it come down to two determined bidders, and they didn't care any more about letting it be known they were in serious need of winning Him and using Him. No more laughing, no more make-believe.

"Two hundred and fifty."

"Two hundred and fifty-five."

"Two hundred and sixty."

It went over three hundred before one of the bidders held up her hand, stopping the action. "Will a . . . will a check be all right?"

"Table stakes," my owner ruled sternly. "Cash on the barrelhead."

The other bidder glanced in triumph at her opponent and said, "Three hundred and fifty," making a twenty-five-dollar jump. Which was the price I went at.

The lady came forward. She didn't look at me whilst finding the money in her purse. But I was looking at the winner.

A nice lady. There might be wrinkles in her neck, but she had a figure she had took care of for a long time. Beautiful eyes, too, and a nice, kind mouth. I began to count myself the lucky one.

Paid in full, she gave me a slow, deep look. Then she leaned to place her mouth on my naked hip, leaving the mark of her lipstick, then stood away, lifting the chain from Him as she did so.

"My brand," she cried out, turning triumphantly to the other ladies, throwing her head back, standing proud and unashamed. Which made the losers applaud such a good winner.

As I climbed down, she said quietly, "Go below

147

decks, I'll be along." Then, to the group again, "I really hate to break up the bridge table," saying it very seriously.

"Don't worry, honey, I'll play your hand for you," Miss Ruby said. Her big laugh boomed out. "Either way, below decks or up here."

I waited, sitting on the bunk in one of the staterooms; but in no time at all she stood in the doorway.

Her voice came low. "I . . . don't know what got into me."

Knowing she just had to tell herself that, I didn't try to answer to it. Instead I said, "Did you bring my gold chain?"

"Yes." She handed it to me. Her mood had changed entirely. "I've . . . never bought a man before."

I put the chain around my neck and smiled at her. "I've never been sold before, either."

She came closer. "Really?"

"Yes'm," I said. "It's my first cruise on the *Liberated Lady*."

"Wonderful," she breathed. "I thought . . ." And then, "Can I do . . . anything I wish?"

"Yes'm," I said. "I reckon so."

She wasn't satisfied with herself yet. "But Miss Ruby . . . she said you had the right to say no."

"Yes," I said.

I was looking at her. Then she was looking at me. She suddenly caught a ragged breath. "Then . . . then take off my clothes."

I did. Piece by piece, as slowly as I could, to give her time to get used to the idea of taking Him. It worked, too. When I had her naked, she just laid down on the bunk, lifting her legs and her arms to receive Him. In the first move, I went so deep it must have hurt, because she moaned and grabbed and hung on.

I want to tell you, that lady—I never did know
148

her name, because she didn't ever take another cruise—just wouldn't quit. She wanted Him every way there was, on and on and on, and every time He thought He was through, she found out how to raise Him from the dead.

Close to the end, she wanted to take Him behind. I didn't know how she meant at first; when I did understand, I said, "Can a woman do it like that?"

"Yes," she said. "Yes!" Then, "I never have, I've never dared ask for it, but I've always wanted . . . and you told me . . ."

"Ain't I likely to hurt you?" I said dubiously.

"Yes," she said wildly. "Hurt me, hurt me, hurt me, damn it, hurt me to the quick," and flopped over on her belly.

It did hurt, easy as I tried to be. She laid there, panting, saying, "I can't stand it, I can't stand it, how can he stand it, oh, God, I can't . . ." but when I'd back off, she'd say, "No, don't quit, damn it, you've got to hurt me."

Finally I just took the bull by the horns and rammed it home. She screamed so loud she must have been heard all over the boat. She laid limp under me, the cold sweat popped out all over her body, and it seemed like she just melted into the mattress, she went so soft and warm. When I started fucking, she began getting the deep comings like I had never known a lady to do before, her whole insides rippling and writhing.

When it was all over, she clung to me for the longest time, quietly weeping, and kissing my chest, and stroking my flanks with her hands, Him slid sideways into her true place, just laying easy in her soft pussy, and I knew for sure that she had got her money's worth.

At which time she said, "So that's how he feels," and I said, "Who?" and she said, "The man I'm married to," and then, "He's that way. I didn't know it

149

until . . ." And she wept again, while I held her. But she never again came aboard the *Liberated Lady*.

That was my introduction to the *Liberated Lady*, where I stayed so long it come to be a way of life that satisfied me more truly than any I had yet known. I had found my place; and I knew it every day that I lived with Miss Ruby; maybe because there was something inside of me—or inside of Billy —that realized it couldn't last forever, that it would all come to an end long before I was ready for an ending.

Which it did.

The Girl

It was pure accident that I came to New Orleans. Or maybe it was meant to happen that way. Take a look back, don't nothing that happens in your life seem like an accident, because you can't figure how it could ever have been any way different. Which makes you to wonder.

How it come about was this. For a week, now, I had been traveling with this one fellow. It was against my rules, but we got along good together. All day long I'd ride shotgun in his big truck—he was driving one of them Peterbilts, with chrome stacks and all, which made him mighty high class amongst the other truck drivers. They all want to drive a "Pete."

Or else I'd get up in the bunk, especially if I'd been entertaining fellows till all hours last night, and doze off, knowing even while I was sleeping that he was rolling me safely down the highway. Just the best long-haul truck driver I ever traveled with. A real gypsy, too, that traveled all over the place. Give him a choice between a milk run and someplace he'd never been before, and there wasn't no doubt about where he'd go.

When we'd pull into a truck stop, he'd go inside first and get me all fixed up—I want to tell you, I was well-known by this time, and the fellows liked hearing that I was on the premises—and then he'd take his dollar turn first of all. After he had got satisfied, he'd go out and sleep in his truck, to save the money for another room, you see, and leave me to my business. First thing in the morning, he'd come in and wash up whilst I was having my breakfast somebody had brought from the restaurant, and then he'd look at me with his pretty black eyes, which had long lashes just like a girl's, though there was certainly nothing girlish about *him*, and he'd say, "Going my way?"

I don't understand to this day why it was, but every time he asked, I'd say, "Well, I reckon I am." I don't know why it was. Maybe it was that he was such a strange fellow, in a nice sort of way. He had this funny way of talking which I just liked to hear, no matter what he happened to be saying, because he was what they call a Cajun. His voice just lilted and sang like a bird. He was dark-complected, with black hair and black eyes, and though not a big man, was built as strong and pretty as that Peterbilt truck he drove so proudly.

One day, just as the sun was going down, we had come into this place called Algiers. He stopped the truck in front of a bus station.

"I will say good-bye to you, Cherie, because tonight I go home."

He always called me Cherie for some reason, though it wasn't anywhere close to my name.

It had come up so sudden, I hadn't been expecting it. "I wish I could go with you," I said. "Ain't been in a house so long, I've forgot what it feels like."

He laughed, showing his white, white teeth. "The fine wife, she take one look at you, she bite my head off," he said. He snapped his teeth. "Just like an old 'gator."

I looked up and down the dingy street, letting myself get a little mad. "What am I going to do in a dump like this? Least you could have done was leave me at the truck stop this morning."

"I wished to travel this day with you," he said quietly. Then he pointed. "There is New Orleans across the river. A fine city. Have you ever been to New Orleans?"

"No," I said shortly.

"Try it. You will like it."

"I ain't no city girl," I said. Then I said, "But I'll go take a look, I reckon. I could use a few days' layover anyway, buy me some clothes and all. So I'll just do that before I hit the road again."

He reached over me to open the door. I got out and stood looking up at him, holding my suitcase in hand. "See you around," I said.

He smiled. "Take good care, Cherie. You are one fine girl."

Turning away before *he* left *me*, I walked into the bus station. It don't do to travel too long with any one fellow, as I well knew; you get an empty feeling when the time comes to go your own way. So I didn't look back when I heard the truck motor start singing its song. He wasn't going nowheres interesting, anyway, just rolling home to his wife.

I found out I didn't need a Greyhound to get to New Orleans; just take a city bus. So I got on one and crossed the big river. I had asked the driver which was the main drag, so I got off at Canal Street. I had decided I was going to use this city, because it had been recommended by a friend.

You see, I had been to lots of big towns, but always only on the outskirts. Chicago, Denver, Spokane, Dallas, Texas—I had lived out my time in those places on the bypasses and interstates where the truck stops were located, where the truck drivers passed their sleeping and resting time.

So it was a whole new experience to get out of the bus on Canal Street and walk around carrying my little suitcase. The sun was just setting, the lights coming on, and there were more people than a body could wonder at. Off to one side, I took note of these narrow little streets that looked just as pretty as a picture postcard from over across the big ocean, iron-railed balconies hanging over the sidewalks and all, so I left Canal Street behind and went in there, looking into the shop windows.

An interesting place if you hadn't ever seen it. I found out later it had a special name, the French Quarter. There were some weird folks populating the place, let me tell you, bums and junkies and tourists, and more bars and cafés than you could use in a hundred years, and all these shops selling strange things I had never seen sold before, old chairs and paintings and real old-timey jewelry and such. It made me to wonder who'd buy all that junk.

I come to a street that was built solid, shoulder-to-shoulder, with bars; fancy places with music coming out, and pictures of women that were durn nigh naked, and men standing in front fast-talking the people to come inside and take in the show. The street was just waking up, this early in the evening, but already people were surging up and down the narrow sidewalks chasing all that entertainment. A lively place.

After a while my feet got to hurting—I never

154

was much of a one to stand on my feet for long at a time—so I started thinking about finding a place to stay. I'd already passed one big hotel, and lots of little ones that, every one, seemed to have these narrow staircases going up to the second floor above the street. I hadn't ever stayed in a real hotel, though, so what I wanted was a nice Ramada Inn, something I was used to. Finally, seeing this quiet little bar on a corner, not one of them places where they were hollering about the girlies girlies girlies they had inside, I went in to see what I could find out.

I didn't take a stool, just stood up to the bar to talk to the bartender. I hadn't no more than took my place than this red-faced fellow sitting on the stool next to me looked over to say, "Now, here's a little girl I aim to buy a drink."

He was wearing a suit and a tie, but he was durn nigh as drunk as Papa used to get. He just reeked of liquor.

"Just climb right up here on this stoool and name your favorite drink." He grinned sort of nasty-like. "O' course, I already know one thing you like. Right?"

I got up on the stool. The bartender moved down to us, swiping at the counter with a rag. "What'll it be?"

"I don't drink," I said.

The red-faced fellow opened his mouth, just bellowing. "The little girlie says she don't drink! Now, how about that?"

The noise made people's heads turn all the way down the length of the bar. Which stirred me up. So I said, "I not only don't drink, I don't like to be breathed on by them that does. If I don't like a fellow breathing on me, I don't want him touching me, neither."

Because by this time he had his big hand heavy on my shoulder.

He got even redder in the face, because the
155

people were looking at him now, and some were laughing. So he glared, saying a cuss word, threw a five-dollar bill on the bar, and walked out.

"Listen," the bartender said, "you can't come in here without ordering a drink."

I smiled nicely. "Can I have a Coke?"

He just automatically grinned back, which I have found that most people will do when I act so whole-hearted with them.

"It'll cost you a dollar," he said to warn me.

"I guess I can stand the tariff one time," I said, taking a dollar out of my purse and placing it before him. "I don't mind telling you, my feet hurt something awful."

He brought the Coke and scuffed up the dollar. "Of course, I don't appreciate you running off my good customers, either."

"Sorry about that," I said. "It's just that I can't stand a man with liquor on his breath."

He laughed. "You've come to the wrong place, then."

"I just come in off the street to see if you could tell me a good place to spend the night," I told him.

He looked at me. "New in town?"

"Sure am," I said. "Since about an hour ago, as a matter of fact."

"There's the Monteleone Hotel over there just a block or two."

I shook my head. "What I'd like more would be a nice motel," I said. "That's what I'm used to."

"There's a Holiday Inn," he said, and told me exactly how to find it. Which was right nice of him. I have found out that most people *will* be nice if you give them the chance to be.

So I sat sipping on my dollar Coke, while the bartender moved away to tend to business. I was thinking that if all the prices in New Orleans measured up to the cost of a Coca-Cola, I would have to think about raising my price again. Wouldn't be like it had been, with the truck drivers paying for my rooms and my meals and all. On the road, a dollar made was a dollar earned. I could tell right now it wasn't going to be so easy on a girl in downtown New Orleans.

The bartender worked his way back to me. "Gonna be around long?"

"I don't know," I said. "I come and I go."

He smiled. "Yeah. I bet you do." Glancing down the bar, then leaning forward, he lowered his voice. "Listen. You'll be a lonesome girl in this town if you don't take up drinking. Not many places you can go without ordering a drink."

"I don't care," I said. "I'll just stay out on the street if I have to."

His eyes turned sharp and thoughtful. "You're not exactly the run-of-the-mill country girl come to town."

"I've been traveling for some time," I told him, smiling again.

He smiled back, ducking his head closer and lowering his voice again. "Listen. If you want to, you can come in here anytime you like. If a fellow offers to buy you a drink, take him up on it."

I started to say something, but he waved his hand.

"What I mean is, I'll set you up a shot of iced tea. Put it in a whiskey glass, looks just like whiskey. The fellow won't ever know the difference."

"Well, that's a pretty good deal for you, all right," I said. "Selling cold iced tea for the price of liquor."

"Yeah, but it means you can come in off the street whenever you feel like it."

I thought about it, studying him all over again.

157

He was a nice enough fellow, sort of slender, with quick hands and an Adam's apple showing over his black leather bow tie.

"Looks like I ought to get something out of it," I said. "I ain't never been all that fond of iced tea, neither."

He shook his head, laughing like it hurt him a little bit. "You *have* been away from home, haven't you?"

I just laughed at him. "A girl's got to look out for herself, that's what I always say."

He looked at me, looked away. "All right. Every glass of tea you drink, you get a quarter. I'll keep count and pay up anytime you want the money. All right?"

"All right," I said. "Except, when I need a Coca-Cola, I want to be able to buy it at its natural price of a dime." I didn't aim to keep on paying a dollar every time, that was for sure. He nodded his head.

I thought it was real clever of him to fix it so I could come in and sit down anytime I wanted, not to mention doing himself, and me, a little bit of good. Of course, I learned right quick that he hadn't invented the idea out of his own head, right then and there, and at that he was short-changing me from the standard going rate. We got that part all fixed up as soon as I brought it to his attention.

I finished my Coke and slid down off the stool. At which, he started polishing at the bar between us.

"Suppose a fellow might pay a visit up there to the Holiday Inn after he gets off work?" he said. He looked up quickly. "That'd be somewhere around two o'clock in the morning."

I smiled sweetly. "Don't know why not," I told him. "Except I don't have the faintest idea, yet, what my room number might be."

"Just tell me your name, and I'll find you," he said quickly.

So I told him, and he told me his name was Eddie, and I turned to go, thinking to myself that it looked like a girl ought to be able to do all right for herself in the big city.

He was polishing at the bar again. "Wait a minute," he said. I waited, but he couldn't find the words. Finally, without looking at me, he said, "You wouldn't mind if a fellow come on sort of strange, would you?"

"Not as long as he don't want to hurt me," I said. "I like to feel good just as much as the next person."

He glanced at me quickly, and then away. "I'll just bet you do," he said. "I'll see you."

I checked in at the motel and took myself the longest, soakiest bath you can imagine. I had got to where I carried bath salts in my suitcase for just such an occasion. I don't know anything that can make you feel better after hard days on the road.

I got naked into bed and was sound asleep when Eddie came knocking at my door. I went yawning and naked as a jaybird to let him in. He took the first look at me, and I heard him draw in his breath. It's nice to have that sort of effect on a nice fellow.

"I'm still half-asleep," I said. "Come on to bed. But . . ." I hadn't given any thought to the problem of city living, so I grabbed the first figure that came into my head. "But I want to tell you. It'll be ten dollars."

It didn't faze him in the least, I was glad to see; he just put his arms around me, saying, "I'll carry you back to bed."

"Give me my money first."

When he handed it over, I looked at the ten-dollar bill. It was another pretty good raise. I *knew*, now, that a girl could make out in the big city.

159

Putting me on the bed, he laid down beside me. Still so sleepy, I didn't know at first what it was he was up to. He hadn't taken off his clothes at all, yet was kissing me so sweet and soft that I just nearly drowsed off with the niceness of it. He did it for a long time, too, without touching me at all. Then he put his mouth down to my breast.

I've always liked a fellow to do that. It must feel like unto when you've got your very own baby nursing at you, so I cradled his head in my arms and let him have his way. I hadn't ever had a man stay with it as long as he did, though, so pretty soon I was halfway to sleep again. It was like there wasn't any hungry need in him for me to satisfy, so I could lay there and feel as cozy as could be.

Then he got to licking his tongue all over my belly and down my thighs, just like a cat, and it brought the goose bumps so that I sat up and tried to make him stop. I didn't have much conviction against it, though, so when he wouldn't leave off, I just let him have his way.

It was like my body knowed something I didn't know, because my legs went so weak and soft, I laid there as flat as a flitter, and helpless to his doings. It was then that he put his mouth between my legs and started fluttering his tongue in an interesting way. It startled me; I hadn't ever thought of any such a thing, and certainly none of my fine truck drivers had, either. I tightened up against him, afraid of what he aimed to do next.

But I couldn't keep it up; it was so nice to be done so. Time had gone away forever, because he wasn't in no hurry, never had been; he had all night and forever to use his tongue in me. It was just the sweetest thing a fellow ever thought to do to a girl; it made me put my hands down on top of his head and push his face into me.

160

That was when he began to speed it up, and I started to move with it in spite of myself, feeling like I was just going to bust if something didn't happen. Always before when I had got to feeling like that with a fellow, I'd put a stop to it. There was this thing in me, you know, that told me, since I was getting paid, it was up to me to pleasure the man, not myself.

But it was more than that. I just couldn't like that feeling of slipping willy-nilly into a state where you don't have the say-so over your own doings, giving the man the using of you in a way he ain't bought and paid for. Now, I'm not claiming it isn't the nicest feeling in the world to have a man's hard old Thing plunging inside of you, going wilder and wilder, so that when he starts he can't help himself no more, he's just got to let it go. That's when a girl who knows her business starts to work, inside there, milking him right on down until he's helpless in your arms, and all limp and used-up inside of you.

So a girl like me, with a right sense of herself, don't want to let it happen to her; though it never had, there had come from time to time a feeling inside myself that maybe, if I wasn't almighty careful, I'd let the man do It to me, instead of doing It to him.

This time, though, it was as different as could be. For one thing, he had his clothes on still, and he hadn't made the first move toward putting his old Thing where his mouth was. Since it wasn't his stiff Thing working me up, I felt like I could afford to let the feeling grow for a little while, just warm and sweet and good, and more and more like I was gonna bust any minute now.

I did bust it. Because, after all this long time, his tongue turned into a flicker of flame, faster and hotter and fiercer, and before I could stop myself, my legs locked around his head and I was fucking not

161

just his tongue but his whole head, a terrible thunder-storm racking through me with quivers of lightning, and I was shaking all inside like a bowl of Jell-O.

Done at last, I hadn't ever felt so good in my life. I had to slide down and put my mouth on his mouth, tasting myself but not caring. I had to kiss him a thousand times, while he started laughing and strug-gling to get away.

"You act like nobody's ever done you before," he said when I finally calmed down and just laid there holding him, holding the fine, finished feeling inside of me at the same time.

"Ain't nobody ever done me *that* way," I said. "Not only that. Ain't no man ever made me act like that, either."

"You mean . . . you haven't ever *come?*"

"So that's what it was," I said. "I thought that was all for the man."

"You mean . . . for the first time in your life, you've found out what you can feel?" He laughed suddenly. "Maybe I ought to make you give me my money back."

I didn't pay any attention to that idea. "A girl, she can't let herself go like a man does," I said. "It ain't right, seems like to me."

"But you just did. God, I thought you were go-ing to strangle me."

I laughed. "You snuck up on me. Or else I'd have put a cold stop to it."

"Aren't you glad you didn't?"

I thought about it. "I reckon so. It's just that, now that I know how a girl can let herself feel, it might be a lot tougher to keep on pleasuring the man instead."

"You've been hustling for a long time, haven't you?"

"Since I was fourteen years old," I said proudly.

162

"Ain't never done it for nothing." I didn't figure I'd mention Papa's free rides. He might not understand how it was.

"And all that time . . ."

"All that time," I said. Twisting around, anxious to keep on, I started to unbutton his shirt. "And all this time I ain't done a thing for you. Let me get your clothes off."

He pushed my hands away. "I don't need that." He had a strange tone to his voice.

"I never knew a man yet didn't need It," I told him, and kept on unbuttoning.

He pushed my hands away again. His voice was all upset this time. "Quit it, now! I've had my kicks."

"You mean to tell me, doing It to a woman like that . . ."

"I *like* a woman that way," he said, his voice backing up. "That's all I need, to taste her, smell her, turn her on. . . ."

"I don't understand," I said slowly. "You really don't want to do It to me?"

"No," he said angrily.

Not liking to see him so mad, I started soothing him with my hands. He laid still for a time, me close beside him, feeling so good and grateful I wished I could do something for him.

Maybe I was, just loving him with my hands, because after a while he said, "All right. I'll tell you. It's just that . . . I can't get it up when I start to put it in." His voice tightened. "I warned you. I told you in front that I was strange, didn't I?"

"I'll bet I can fix it, if you'll just let me have my way," I said.

"No," he said. "I've tried it too many times."

"Come on!" I said. "Don't be like that."

He was drawing away. "I've always been like
163

that. First woman I ever had, she laughed at me because I was so nervous about It. Every time I tried It since, I had this feeling the woman was laughing, whether she was or not, and so I . . ."

"I'm not laughing, am I?" I said tenderly. "Come on, now. Let me take your clothes off."

I wouldn't let him say me nay. It took a lot of begging, and a lot of time, but finally I got him naked.

"Now, you just stand up there and let me look at you," I said, pushing him off the bed.

I turned on the bedside lamp. He was a pretty young fellow, as skinny as a rail, with fair skin and fair hair.

"You look just fine to me," I told him.

And he did. Except that his old Thing just hung there.

"It's no good, I tell you," he said, gazing down woefully upon himself. His mouth tightened. "I even tried the queer route. I let myself be trade for the gay boys in this town. I could get it off, all right, but I just didn't like being done by men."

"You ain't sick or anything?"

He moved his shoulders. "No. It's that . . ."

I switched out the light and reached my hand to cuddle his Thing. "Then come here. You done a new thing for me tonight. Now I aim to do a new thing for you."

He came to me, all right; at least, he was trusting enough to try. But where a man's weakness is concerned, willingness ain't never enough. I laid there in the dark, holding him close and peeling his Thing with a nice warm hand, and didn't do nothing for him.

Then I started talking. First I told him how he had made me feel, like no man had ever done before, and how he was some kind of a man to be ready,

164

willing, and able to do a girl like he had done me.

Still nothing. So then I got him on top, opening my legs and putting both hands to his butt to press him close, and in his ear I was still telling him he was the mightiest man I had ever known because he had brought me to the edge and over it, where I hadn't ever been before.

"No woman in the world could laugh at a man with that kind of doings to him," I whispered. "You didn't catch me laughing, did you? I wanted to cry, it felt so good."

For the first time, I felt the least little bulge. So then I reached down between my legs and took hold of his old Thing again, gripping tight just at the base, and rubbed the head against me.

While I was doing that, I was thinking inside myself, not just telling him, how I had felt with his mouth on me. Thinking about it made me feel it all over again, not all the way, but enough, anyway, so that I could reach out and take him inside, limp though it was.

It just laid there, but I kept on thinking, not talking out loud anymore, and I moved under him with the thinking, feeling his Thing so small and soft it felt like his tongue, didn't it, except it didn't yet have the striking power.

He held himself so still, as if scared to make the least move; but, shoot, once it started growing, there wasn't no stopping it, not with me wrapped around his old Thing to help. It was all of a sudden *there*, and he started to move too, pushing slow and easy like he didn't believe it. I started going like a house afire under him—and my little house *was* on fire with all that remembering, let me tell you—and it brought him up and running before he knew it.

He climbed all the way to it, quicker than you'd believe. At the last minute, though, he lost confidence and backed off, going nearly as limp as at first starting. Patiently I started all over again, holding his Thing in with my hand and working against him until he started a comeback.

That was when I got a big idea; I started playing like I was losing control again. Boy, that did the trick! Before I knew it, he was plunging and carrying on like a stud horse, with a hard-on that just wouldn't quit, and the next thing I knew, I wasn't playacting either, but going for the real thing. So we come to it together, and it was a fine something, better even than the first time, and I didn't even care that it had been his old Thing and not his tongue that had done It to me.

Holding each other, we went off easy to sleep, to wake up together in the morning—and that was a first-time something for me, too. But somehow or other neither one of us wanted to risk it again. It was not only that we were afraid it wouldn't work; we didn't *need* to take the chance.

Eddie didn't have to go to work till six o'clock in the evening, so we stayed together the livelong day, eating breakfast and lunch in the room, talking and getting to know each other. Before he finally left, we did do it one more time—me telling him, of course, it would be another ten dollars now—and by this time he had reached such confidence he didn't have the least bit of trouble, and afterward kept strutting around the room, slow to get dressed because he wanted to admire his successful old Thing in the mirror. It made me sad to think that it hadn't crossed his mind to use his tongue to do me this time; but at least I felt proud to have made him a full man.

He finally had to go, or miss getting to work on time. Before finally leaving, though, he said, "Look, I want to tell you something. You can get fifty dollars a trick in this town."

166

"*Now* you tell me," I said, laughing. "Why didn't you say so when you first got here?"

He laughed, too. "Because I couldn't have afforded the price. But, look, just the sleaziest old streetwalker can knock down twenty, twenty-five. You're so young and so pretty, fifty dollars is not too much to ask." He laughed again. "Why, tell a man in New Orleans he can have It for ten dollars, he'll think you've got a disease or something."

"All right," I said. "I always did want to be rich. You just got the last ten-dollar piece of ass I'll ever put out." I didn't tell him it was the first, too.

He got an anxious look to his face. "But . . . look, I can see you when I want to, can't I? I mean . . . me and you, we've got something going."

He sounded so upset, I had to think about it. But if a girl's got rules, she's got to stick to them, ain't she?

"Eddie, I ain't never given It to nobody for nothing," I said. "I . . . I just wouldn't feel right, not getting paid."

His face was miserable. "I just find you, and then I talk myself out of It," he said. He made a face. "Looks like I'd learn to keep my big mouth shut."

I laughed. "I hope you don't ever do that." He was still so miserable, I went to put my arms around his waist. "Tell you what, Eddie, you can always have It at the old price. All right? Nobody else, but ten dollars will get It anytime. All right?"

Smiling in relief, he kissed me and hurried to work. And thinking about it, I felt all right about my bargain with Eddie. Because after all, I told myself secretly, not quite letting myself know what I was thinking, he's giving you a lot, too. You can let go with him. Which was a fine thing to know, because I hadn't ever felt so good in body and soul as I did right then.

167

But little did I know that that one little change in my way of life, making a special price for a special man, would bring about such enormous changes in the person that I knew myself to be.

The Boy

Miss Ruby was just about the nicest old lady I've ever known, and that was why I stayed with her. It got to where she didn't hardly ever use the other boys, except once in a while to break in a new fellow on the job.

I got to know all about her. She told me she was Texas-raised, on a hardscrabble ranch where, according to her, the cattle were leaner than the coyotes, and twice as mean. It come about, the year she was eighteen, her folks were killed in an automobile accident, right after oil had been struck on their land. Overnight, Miss Ruby had become an orphan and what you might call wealthy, if not downright rich. She didn't have to run the *Liberated Lady* for a living; it was only a means of keeping her hand in with her main interests in life, gambling and people.

"I perform a real service," she told me. "On the *Liberated Lady*, these women can let their hair down

169

and just have a good time, not only gambling away their money, but by taking advantage of one of you nice boys—or just *thinking* about it, if that suits them."

She told me how she herself had gone hog-wild at eighteen with all that money. First it was gambling in Nevada, then the sporting clubs in London, England, and afterward that place in Europe called Monte Carlo that everybody talks about all the time as being just the finest gambling in the world. In between, it was racetracks all over the world; she didn't miss a big race, and having her bet down.

"I used up much of the money; after all, there was more coming out of the ground every day," she told me. "But I had my fun doing it. Why, when I was thirty, I had my very own gigolo, a Frenchman who not only knew all there was to making love, but could also cook and serve a wonderful meal. He stayed with me ten years, until he had saved enough money to go home, marry his childhood sweetheart, and start raising a family."

Finally she had come home to the United States because the wells weren't pumping as much as they used to; besides, she had pretty much burned out her own personal gambling fever. So she moved to New Orleans, where for several years she lived the life of a lady of leisure.

How she got into the gambling-boat business, she had a chance to buy a nice boat on the cheap, from a fellow who had gone broke, and she used it, at first, to take her society friends out for a weekend on the Gulf, you know, just to drink and dance and fish and swim and have themselves a time. At first it was men *and* women, but she soon found out that people were likely to get drunk, and get in bed with other men's wives, all such chancy doings as that.

"Along about then, I began paying attention to this new movement called women's lib," Miss Ruby
170

told me most thoughtfully. "I got awfully interested. One day it occurred to me there wasn't any reason in the world why women couldn't go out on a cruise, say, and just have themselves a good time without their men around to spoil it. Men do it all the time, don't they? Hunting or fishing in all-male groups, going to conventions where they'll screw any little chippie they can lay their hands on, and it's all just fine and dandy—the wives are supposed to be understanding and forgiving . . . or at best, pretend they don't know what's going on. What's sauce for the gander is sauce for the goose, I decided; one day, when we pulled out from the marina, the ladies were surprised to find there were no men aboard—except two handsome lads I had hired for crew."

She laughed.

"It was a marvelous success. But, to my own surprise, they were most interested in gambling, not sex. We hadn't cleared the breakwater before bridge was going for high stakes, and one group was down on their knees shooting craps."

She kept the cruises going, the first had been so successful. One day a friend told her, "Ruby, I simply wait in suspense every weekend, hoping you'll invite me again. I wish I could volunteer to be your guest whenever I like—especially when my husband's out of town."

Which gave Miss Ruby to think. She traded the boat in on a larger one, which was the *Liberated Lady*, and let it be known quietly amongst her lady friends that they could come along anytime they wanted to, since it was now a commercial proposition. From that day she had never lacked for a full passenger list, glad and able to pay their way.

Miss Ruby was just a bighearted woman. Those nights when me and her would get all cozied up in her purple stateroom, it wasn't all just banging each other—though she took her gusto in that, too, let me

171

tell you, like getting in bed with a Texas bronc—but for hours at a time we'd lay together and talk. That's when she told me all about herself; then, surprisingly enough, she'd tell me about me. She paid attention, you see, though never prying into a person's private life.

I reckon I talked more to Miss Ruby than any nice lady I'd ever met, even including Charlotte Ainsley. I told her about my old ladies, how I felt about them, and once or twice got to wondering out loud why I couldn't seem to get to first base with a girl of my age—or want to, for that matter. I hadn't ever in my life, I told her, taken a date to a school dance or a football game.

Miss Ruby was so loving and friendly, at times I felt moved to talk to her about Billy, my twin brother who had died of a fever when me and him were nine years old. I didn't ever quite do it; I hadn't talked to anybody about Billy since the day I watched him get buried. It wasn't that I didn't *want* to. I just didn't know the words to use, how he was always with me, making it necessary to live every day for Billy as well as for myself. When I got to feeling like that, I'd put my head on her breast, my arms around her big, strong body, and hold her tight whilst she smoothed my hair with her gentle hand. Which was something I hadn't ever done before with any old lady of my acquaintance, nor felt the need of it, either.

One thing Miss Ruby was curious about was, what did I plan to make out of my life.

"Son, you're marvelous and young and full of loving," she told me more than once. "But time's going to catch up with you, you know. When you can't depend on your old ladies anymore, what will become of you?"

I didn't know. I didn't want to think about it. I couldn't see, day by day, that I was getting any older,

172

anyway, like other people seemed to do. But, still, she'd cause me to think about Charlotte Ainsley's statue, and wonder where it was now, who was looking at it and enjoying it. Time might catch up with me, like Miss Ruby said, but it sure wouldn't catch up with that work of art.

It must have been most of a year later when Miss Ruby brought me a clipping out of *The New York Times* newspaper telling about Charlotte Ainsley's latest New York exhibition. The story even showed a picture of the statue, except that it was taken from such an angle as to miss Him entirely, which I didn't think was fair to the interested reader. It seemed that Charlotte Ainsley's new show was just the talk of the town in that great city, just like she had known it would be when she went to work on the idea. It made me proud all over to read what the fellow had to say about it—most of the write-up had to do with that one piece of sculpture. Though I couldn't understand the half of his considerations about it all.

"You're famous, son, did you know that? Though in a peculiarly anonymous way," Miss Ruby told me, laughing.

I gazed at her. "I'm not just famous. I'm immortal."

She nodded soberly. "I guess you are." Then, seriously harking back to her main concern, "But what will you do with the rest of your life? You don't want to have reached your peak at sixteen years of age, do you?"

"It was a pretty good peak," I said, holding tight inside of myself because I didn't want to bother my head about it. "It was a something that could do a fellow for a long time."

Still, I couldn't help but fret about it from time to time. Knowing full well she had my best interests at heart, I had to recognize that she was a couple of hundred miles wiser than I'd ever be. Of course, I'd tell myself every time that my life was just fine. Maybe those ladies were mostly interested in gambling; but, not to mention an occasional drawing for the grand door prize, from time to time I caught an eye —more often than any of the other crewmen, let me tell you that. I didn't take money from them, of course, except maybe a dollar here or a dollar there when otherwise it would have hurt their feelings.

But every one of those ladies, sooner or later, got it in their heads they ought to bring me a nice gift. I had more fancy cufflinks than a fellow could know what to do with . . . especially when I didn't have a shirt to my name I could use them with. Cigarette lighters, too, often sporting diamonds or other jewels, when I didn't even smoke. Wristwatches, and bracelets to wear, made out of fine metals, maybe with their name and mine engraved in linked letters. One lady even wanted me to wear a slave bracelet on my ankle.

This junk got to be such a burden, finally I paid a visit to a jewelry store, where I made a deal with the fellow to buy the stuff. It was always at a good price for him, of course, but at least I got rid of the stuff. Made me sort of uneasy, selling it for money like that, but I finally settled in my head how it didn't make me a hustling stud in any form or fashion, because as far as I was concerned it was just useless junk and, after all, a fellow could use some walking-around money from time to time.

Naturally, I kept the golden chain Charlotte Ainsley had placed around my neck. I was never without it, because the weight of it hanging on my chest reminded me of that great time in my life. There was one fine wristwatch, too, with all these dials and stems, which is called a chronometer, that had my first name etched out in tiny sparkling diamonds, which I kept, and a couple of nice rings, one

174

a ruby and one a diamond. They weren't gaudy at all, just nice quiet rings that a fellow could take pleasure in seeing on his hands.

Right after she showed me *The New York Times* piece, Miss Ruby made up her mind about my future. Not that she told me right off the bat what she had in mind; she just started taking me around town, nights we weren't out on the boat, so that I got to see the fine places she went to, private clubs, gambling places, all that. I figured she only wanted a friendly escort, and was pleased to do it for her; but without my realizing it, she was teaching me how to carry myself in such fine surroundings, how to use a knife and a fork in the right way, how to carry on polite conversations with friends and strangers.

Of course, she had to outfit me with the proper clothes for such doings—even including some shirts with French cuffs, so the next couple of cufflinks gifted to me I kept instead of selling—and began correcting my grammar, so that when I wanted to I could talk just the same as all her fine friends.

Oh, I tell you, I cut such a figure alongside Miss Ruby—lighting her cigarette when she wanted it lit, making polite conversation, dancing with her now and again—many was the envious glance cast at her from other ladies. She had sent me to this school of dance to learn all the South American tangos and sambas and so forth, where I found out right quickly that, light on my feet as I was, any lady could be proud to hold me as her dancing partner.

One night she took me to a formal dinner, dinner jacket and all the rest of it—one of those meals where nobody gets to sit next to the person they had thought enough of to come there with—so that I had to deal with these two stranger ladies, each of whom seemed to want all my attention. Which didn't make the situation any easier, let me tell you. Miss Ruby, who kept an eye on me all evening, must have been

175

satisfied with my public conduct, because when we got back to the *Liberated Lady* she told me the plan she had worked out.

"What you must do, son, is find the right lady and stick with her," she said. "It's time you began to make something of your great talent instead of squandering it heedlessly as you have been doing."

"But, Miss Ruby," I said, "I've told you a dozen times. I ain't nobody's stud. I just can't take money from a nice lady. I couldn't feel right about it, and that's all there is to it."

She looked at me for a full minute. "There's nothing shameful about such an arrangement. It's done all the time. Besides, once we find the lady you can take great joy in serving, I'll personally work out the details. I'll fix it so that, in time, you'll have accumulated enough money to manage with on your own."

I shook my head. "I'd know it, even if I didn't see the first dollar," I told her. "I can't do good to any old lady just because she's bought and paid for Him. She thinks."

She kept on regarding me. "You've got it now, son. Use it while you've got it." She was very patient. "Don't you see? It's only what you have always done for your ladies. The money is not for now, but for the future. What's wrong in that?"

I didn't answer.

She leaned forward. "Believe me, son, it'll be so right, it won't cost you one twinge of your delicate conscience. I realize that I must not only find someone who can afford you, but who will need you far more than anyone ever has. Will you trust me?"

I didn't look at her. "Why can't it keep on being you?" I said. "I'm satisfied. I don't want to leave you, not ever. And you don't have to pay me no more than what you do already to work on the *Liberated Lady*."

She smiled sadly. "I have no wish to lose you, either. But . . . I squandered so much in my young-

176

er days, I can't afford to do for you what I feel must be done." She paused, then went on in this rough tone of voice. "Besides, I've got to stop worrying about you all the time. Once you're set in life as advantageously as I can manage it, I can wash my hands of you." Her voice changed again. "But you'll have to trust me."

"You know I trust you," I said. "But . . ."

She laughed. "But nothing. Just let me handle it. All right? I won't do you dirt."

"I never did think that. It's just that . . ."

She punched me on the shoulder with a doubled-up fist. "Shut up, son, and let Miss Ruby find your nice lady who can afford to keep Him in the style he deserves. I'm not doing this for you, anyway, it's all for Him."

Which was a whole new angle I hadn't thought about; after all, being the best, he deserved the best, didn't he? Maybe, I told myself, all this time I've been cheating Him of his rightful dues, except that one time with Miss Charlotte.

From then on, when we went out, it was always with another lady or two. Just a friendly party; except that Miss Ruby secretly watched them with me, and me with them, because, she told me, she had already decided through other investigation they were all possible candidates. It made me feel sort of awkward at first, but it went on so long—she couldn't ever seem to locate exactly the lady to satisfy her standards for Him—pretty soon I just went back to being my natural self, which had got me through life pretty good so far in spite of all Miss Ruby's fretting about my uncertain future.

There were two ladies she recommended that I try out, one just for a night, the other for a long weekend on a great big plantation somewhere up the Mississippi River. I really did like the second one, a tall woman with coal-black hair and a Frenchified face, who looked haughty as all hell but after I had got done with her just turned into the warmest kitten you ever petted. She liked me, also, to the point that she and Miss Ruby got down to brass tacks. Later on, when we didn't see her again, Miss Ruby remarked that the French are just the stingiest people on God's green earth.

During this time, I got to know New Orleans in both the high and the low. It *was* a various town. One night we'd be out on Lake Pontchartrain at a quiet private club where gambling went on, another time in a nightclub on Bourbon Street where ladies would take off their clothes to music. One night, I remember, we went to a rooster fight where everybody but our party was black, and money changed hands so fast, and the excitement was so high, you couldn't have kept track if you'd had a dozen eyes. We went over into Mississippi to see a dogfight, in which one of these tough, all-muscle-and-mouth dogs just naturally killed down the other one. I didn't like it very much, though I hadn't much minded the game roosters fighting with them long steel spurs and killing one another just as dead. It didn't seem right to do such to a dog, no matter how mean he might be in his nature.

There were genteel parties in private houses, where everybody stood around with a drink in their hands and talked to one another about nothing at all. One time we went to hear this great big orchestra play a symphonic sort of music, and again to hear four old guys playing that good Dixieland stuff, all of them white of hair and wrinkled of face, they'd been around for so long, but when they got into "Muskrat Ramble," or something like that, you'd have thought they was sixteen years old and at their peak.

The curiousest thing I remember about all this going around New Orleans to take in the sights was the sex show we saw one night. It took place in this

178

awfully plush place, a whorehouse, I reckon, to give it its rightful name, though it was a mighty high-class whorehouse. The funny thing about this sex show was, it wasn't just men there to see it, but ladies, too—ladies who didn't *work* there, I mean, but had paid cash money to see the acts they put on.

It was something, all right. I sat there with Miss Ruby and these two ladies she had brought along to meet me, and watched it all. You wouldn't believe what all went on if I told you. They had a great big white German shepherd dog that had been trained in ways strange to see. They had a billygoat, living in billygoat heaven if there is such a thing. They even had this little jackass—except he wasn't so little where it counted—and I couldn't believe my eyes when a woman laid down under him and not only took all he had to offer, but actually acted like she was overjoyed with it. There was a woman who had trained herself to go around and pick up half-dollars off the tables with her pussy, which was something to see how she'd do it; except some smart-aleck held a cigarette lighter to his half-dollar, getting it all heated up before he laid it on the edge of the table. It didn't take her hardly any time at all to find out what he'd done, either, and she started cussing and hitting him over the head with her fists, which pretty much brought the show to a standstill for a few minutes.

I took a natural interest in the men who worked in the show. There were three or four of them, one with a whip, but the others just with their natural-born equipment. I must say, I didn't see anything remarkable that would bring them to such great stardom.

Miss Ruby agreed with me about that. How I know is, after the show was over, this lady who owned the place came over to say hello. Miss Ruby, after congratulating her on her fine sex show, laid

179

her hand on my arm and said proudly, "Of course, I must say, this lad would put any of your boys to shame."

The owner glanced toward me, smiling. "I'll take your word for it, Miss Ruby." Then, to me, "Anytime you need a good job, just come around and see me."

"Oh, no," Miss Ruby said, laughing and shaking her head. "I've got bigger plans. His cock has already made him immortal, and now, if I have my way about it, it'll make him rich."

I was glad the two candidates weren't there to hear all this—they had gone off somewhere for the moment—because then Miss Ruby began to explain about Charlotte Ainsley's work of art and what a sensation it had created in New York. It interested her friend, too, who kept looking me over with her shrewd eyes.

While I stood listening, little did I know how big a part this sex show I had seen tonight would play in my real and actual future.

Which came about as follows.

One night on a cruise, about four o'clock in the morning, Miss Ruby suddenly buzzed my stateroom. I happened to have a lady with me, but the minute I heard it, I got up and went, because Miss Ruby hadn't ever called me at that time of night, and I just knew in my bones there was something to it.

When I got there, Miss Ruby was sitting up on the side of her big bed, still dressed, holding her hand gripped to her chest.

"Get me a drink of whiskey," she said, gasping out the words. "Then tell Captain Phoebe to take this boat in as fast as she can."

I didn't stand on my two feet; grabbing the decanter of sour mash, I poured a glass half full, put my arms around her shoulders, and held it to her mouth, making her gulp down a healthy shot. Then I laid her back on the bed and ran to wake up Captain Phoebe.

"Miss Ruby's took bad sick," I said. "Make a run for the marina, and call in on the radio to have an ambulance waiting."

When I got back to Miss Ruby, she was sitting up again, doubled over against the pain. I poured another glass of whiskey and made her drink again, after which, believing it would be better for her, I eased her down on the bed again. She laid there, gasping hard and sweating cold blood—her gown was soaked, and her face looked to be a hundred years old—but in a minute or two she had to sit up.

When I tried the whiskey yet again, she pushed it away. By now the boat was under way; I could hear the rumble of the big twin Chryslers, and the water slipping along the hull.

"What's the matter, Miss Ruby?" I begged, hardly able to hear my own voice, I was so scared.

She was some easier now, though still showing the cold sweat. "I don't know," she whispered. "I think it's my heart."

That did scare me. I stood there watching her, not knowing what to do. She finally laid back, letting out a big sigh. Since she seemed to be some better, I took the opportunity to run up to the big lounge. It was a bridge night; the ladies were still playing.

"Any of you ladies know anything about doctoring?" I said. "Miss Ruby's mighty bad sick."

They all said no and kept on dealing out new hands. I went on up to the bridge. Captain Phoebe was there, and one of the crewmen.

"She's took bad, and not a soul on board knows anything to do," I told Captain Phoebe, my voice shaking. "Miss Ruby says she thinks it's her heart."

"I was just on my way with the first-aid kit," Captain Phoebe said. To the crewman she said, "Steer for that light yonder, and keep her flat out. I'll be back as soon as I can."

Miss Ruby was sitting up again, bent over and

181

gasping. Captain Phoebe opened the first-aid kit and broke a capsule of ammonia under her nose. Miss Ruby drew in the deepest breath she had taken yet, and collapsed.

"Bring the emergency oxygen," Captain Phoebe snapped at me. "Know where it is?"

I brought it on the run. Captain Phoebe put the mask to Miss Ruby's face and adjusted the tank valves to start it feeding. It brought the color back, so she didn't look so much like death warmed over.

"I must get back to the wheel," Captain Phoebe said. "Watch her. If there's any change, let me know."

The oxygen seemed to be doing the trick, all right. She laid easy during the long run in, breathing it in, while I sat and looked at her, hurting inside. We didn't speak. But I held her hand as they loaded her into the ambulance, then got in to go with her to the hospital.

Miss Ruby got through that first attack all right. I stayed with her until noon the next day, when they moved her out of intensive care. After I'd got some sleep, I went back, as soon as they'd let me in, to find her right chipper to have passed such a rough time. She told me, though, that the doctor had ordered her to stay in the hospital at least a month, and afterward she'd have to take it easy for a long time, no late hours to overtire herself, anything like that.

"I suppose I shall have to give up the *Liberated Lady*."

"Yes'm," I said, feeling sad to think about it. "I reckon so."

It didn't bother me half as much, though, as the mortal fear that dwelled now in her eyes. She had been brushed by the wing of old death, all right, and she'd know it the rest of her days.

I came daily to see her, spending as much time as they'd allow. When I couldn't be at the hospital, I stayed aboard the *Liberated Lady*, scrubbing the

182

decks and polishing the brightwork, because I couldn't seem to sit idle for a minute. Nobody there any more but me and Captain Phoebe, because as soon as the other fellows understood there wouldn't be any more cruises, they took off.

On the fourth day, when I went to the hospital, there was somebody else in her bed. I hurried to the nurses' station to ask where they'd moved her.

"Oh, she's dead," the nurse said, scarcely looking up from her work. "She died last night."

I must have made some sort of sound, because she did look then, saying in a kinder voice, "Oh, I'm sorry. Are you her son?"

"No'm," I said, choking out the words. "But I loved her."

I still think it was a hell of a way to let a fellow know.

I went to Miss Ruby's funeral, of course, but I don't want to talk about it right here and now. A mighty lot of folks turned out to pay their respects, let me tell you, from every walk of life.

After it was over, I went back to the boat, where I put all my stuff into the nice leather suitcase Miss Ruby had bought for me when she had furnished my fine clothes, and for the last time I walked away from the *Liberated Lady*.

Hard days had come upon me. Not only from grieving for Miss Ruby, which I did every waking minute; but it seemed like I couldn't find me a job of honest work to save my life. First I went around to all the little corner grocery stores there in the French Quarter, thinking, since Miss Ruby's great plans for my future had fallen though, I might as well start over again at the beginning.

But not one of those stores was in the least interested in providing delivery service for their good customers. One owner even laughed and said, "Let 'em tote 'em themselves, do 'em good." I offered to

183

work for nothing as far as the store was concerned, depending on tips for the service I could provide, but he yawned in my face.

Money, I found out, don't go hardly noplace in a fancy town like New Orleans. At first I was sleeping in cheap little hotels, but after pawning the suitcase and all my fine clothes, I had to give that up. Within a few weeks I was down to the one suit of clothes and sleeping wherever I could find a place—in the bus station until a cop would come to hustle me, in an alley somewhere, like unto that.

It was at this time, while walking around at night getting tired enough to sleep where I knew I'd have to, that I got offers from these fellows. I hadn't ever had but one man to do his thing on Him, which was Mr. William back home in Pass Robín. Since I hadn't ever thought much of that way of doing, I turned down these anxious fellows—until I had run out of eating money altogether and began feeling the pangs of hunger.

So I had at the last come down to nothing at all. I had made *Him* nothing. Because here I was being a stud for the first time in my life, letting weird men use Him for cold cash, in ways I hadn't even known about when I was young and innocent. It was the bottom, all right. Just as low as a fellow can get and still call himself a human being.

Then, one day, I happened to be sitting in Jackson Square when this woman stopped alongside the bench. "Well, hello," she said. She sounded surprised. I *was* sort of dirty and bedraggled, I must admit.

It was the woman who owned that fancy whorehouse; I recognized her right away. I stood up and said, "Hello. Nice to see you."

"What are *you* doing here?" she said.

Her eyes so sharp and hard on my face, I didn't try to lie. "Not much of nothing, to tell the truth."

"I read about Miss Ruby dying," she said. "As a

184

matter of fact, I had the girls send flowers . . . the nicest wreath." She kept on studying me. "I would presume she didn't get you fixed for life, as she planned."

"No'm," I said. Then I hurried to add, "It wasn't her fault. It was just that . . . Miss Ruby was the finest lady I've ever known in my life, bar none."

"She was that," the lady said. "And more." She stood silent for a moment. Then she said, "Hungry?"

"Yes'm. I ain't ate today." I didn't mention yesterday.

Looking in her purse, she took out a card. "I'm going shopping just now. But come along in an hour or so to this address, and I'll see that you get a square meal."

"That's mighty kind of you, ma'am," I said, taking the card.

She smiled in her frosty way. "I haven't forgotten what Miss Ruby told me about you. So don't disappoint me. I want to talk to you."

"I sure will," I said gratefully.

That was how I come to be a part of the sex show—when, the night I had watched it, so high and mighty, it had been the furtherest thing from my mind. Life sure does take a fellow in strange ways sometimes, don't it? Because, out of all that grief and all that hunger, being down so far I couldn't see any way up, it turned out to be the best thing that ever happened.

The Girl

New Orleans was just fine. After a week, I couldn't understand why I had spent all that time traveling from place to place in order to find new fellows with whom to practice my trade. Everybody in the world, it seems like, comes to New Orleans sooner or later, with good times on their minds. I want to tell you, they came to have fun, too; it wasn't any trouble to do all the business I felt like doing.

Not wanting to use my private quarters at the Holiday Inn for business purposes—except to see Eddie, which wasn't *entirely* business—I went across the street the very first night to talk to the clerk of a little rooming hotel there. We fixed it up between us that I could have the use of a room anytime I wanted it, and in between he'd see there was clean sheets and towels.

Of course, right at first we had something of a

misunderstanding. "It'll be ten dollars an hour," he said. "Cash on the barrelhead." He grinned at me. "No credit cards, not in this fleabag."

I frowned. "That's pretty strong room rent," I said. "You mean I got to shell out ten whole dollars every time I walk in the door? And if my fellow lasts longer than the hour, it's *another* ten?"

"If you know your business, won't many last that long," he said, grinning again. He seemed to like thinking about it.

I shook my head. "I don't know. It's right much, seems like to me."

His voice got real impatient. "It's no skin off your sweet ass, dear. In fact, it's money in your pocket. The john pays for the room . . . and you get half. Whack it up between us, see, the john and the hotel management will never know the difference."

"John?" I said.

"Your customer, for God's sake," he said. "When did you get in from the country, dear?"

"I've been on the road," I said, sort of absent-minded, because I was thinking. "It don't seem fair to me," I went on. "The fellow pays me, open and aboveboard, and I don't see why I need to knock down on him. I'd a lot rather make it five dollars, and let you keep it for yourself."

He grinned again. "Long as I get mine, you can *have* a heart of gold, for all I care."

"All right, then, that's settled." I turned to go. "See you soon, I hope. Be sure there's clean sheets, now."

His eyes ran over me suddenly, like little mice. "Of course, a fellow would expect to lay claim to a free sample from time to time," he said. "Can I count on that?"

I just looked at him. "Ain't no free samples. It'll cost you the same as any other john."

He got red in the face, and mad about the mouth,
187

but I just went on. I didn't aim to bust my rules for nobody. I didn't know it at the time, but I would pay my dues for that cute little remark.

I did have to bend my rules about whiskey drinking, for the simple reason that I operated out of the bar where Eddie worked. So, willy-nilly, they did have liquor on their breaths, and for the first week it made me uneasy every time, until I got used to it. I reckon you can get used to anything, once you set your mind to it. Of course, I drew the line at dog-drunk, or even close. But, I decided, a couple or three drinks would have to be all right, given the situation as it was. A girl has to bend a little bit, sometimes, to get along, the way this world runs.

From the very first night, then, I was in business in a way that, if I didn't watch out, I'd wind up rich. But my first customer—well, actually, he didn't turn out to *be* the first, though I didn't know it at the time —turned out to be right funny, though at the time what happened made me as mad as fire.

It was like this. I hadn't been in Eddie's bar more than ten minutes before he came over to buy me a drink. I sipped the iced tea and watched him take his drink, which he had brought in his hand, and ordered another one. Right off, he told me his name, which was Spence. A nice-looking fellow, but it was plain to see he was from out in the country somewhere, because his face was all brown, and his hands looked like they knew what it was to do a day's work. He was wearing a blue suit with a red-striped tie, pulled loose around his neck, and you could tell he aimed to have him a high old New Orleans time if it killed him.

After he had ordered his second drink, Spence looked at me and said straight out, "Well, girl, how about it?"

"How about what?" I said.

He had just been running on his nerve, I saw

right away, because he blushed and looked away. "I mean . . . you know what I mean."

"I reckon I do," I said. "But I want to warn you. It ain't for free."

"I figured," he mumbled. "How much do you charge?"

"Fifty dollars," I said.

The price troubled him; I could tell he hadn't expected it to be near that much. Which made me wonder just how much money he had on him.

"It's worth it," I told him. "In fact, if you ain't downright satisfied that you ain't never had nothing better, I'll let you have half the money back."

Now, that was a square deal if I do say so myself. I didn't plan to make a practice of guaranteeing satisfaction, but I sort of liked this plain old country boy. Besides, I was anxious to get started.

"Would you really do that?"

"Just try me and see."

He made a firm decision. "All right. You got a place to go?"

"Yes," I said. "But it'll cost you five dollars more for the room."

"For all night?"

"Just for an hour." He was still hesitating, so I said, "Look, it could have been ten dollars just as easy, of which I would have got five. Except I like to be honest and aboveboard."

He looked at me for a minute. Then he said very seriously, "I believe you. So I'll do it."

I glanced toward Eddie, and he nodded. It was a signal he had fixed between us to let me know that, in his experienced opinion, it was all right to go with this particular fellow. So I took Spence by the hand and led him to the door.

It happened just as we stepped onto the sidewalk. One of these willowy kind of chaps, of which you get so many in the French Quarter, boldly

189

grabbed my customer by the other hand, saying, "You don't want to go with *that* thing, darling. You want to come with me."

It bewildered Spence something awful; not knowing what to do, he just stood there between us.

"What are you up to?" I said to the chap. He had this real pretty face, all made up with false eyelashes and everything, and he was dressed to the nines in pretty blue slacks and an embroidered shirt that both fitted him so tight it was like wearing a second skin.

"I can just tell he'd a lot rather go with me," he said, simpering. He already had his hand in Spence's crotch, right there on the street with people passing by. "Wouldn't you, darling boy?"

"I don't know," Spence said. "I ain't never tried it."

The chap was leaning on him now, his other arm tight around Spence's waist. "Oh, darling, you're just in for the biggest thrill of your life." He pouted his mouth. "Besides, she'll charge you the earth for her little golden twat, while with me it won't cost you a thing. Not a *thing!*" He looked daggers at me. "Because *I'm* not a cheap little hustler who'll sleep with just anybody who walks down the street."

"Listen," I said. "Why don't you mind your own business, and let me mind mine?"

He snarled at me, "Fuck off, fish! Can't you see he's trade, whether he knows it or not?"

I didn't exactly know what he meant by calling me a fish, but I reckoned from the tone of his voice that he didn't mean nothing good. So that was when I hit him in the belly with my purse.

He just doubled over, screeching like a cat, "She's killing me. The whore bitch is killing me!"

Which, naturally, drew a crowd. People passing by stopped to stare, whilst others up and down the

190

block began to hurry to take in the trouble, like people will do. The chap straightened up and grabbed Spence's arm with both hands, pulling him away while screeching the durndest streak of cuss words at me you ever heard. He did have a foul mouth. I wasn't going to knuckle under to that, so I grabbed Spence's other arm to keep him from going with the chap, and started hollering too, giving just as good as I was getting.

So there we were, circled by a crowd of people, me hauling Spence one way while the willowy chap hauled him the other. It made me as mad as a wet hen to find myself caught up in public doings like unto that. So I swung my purse again, aiming for the chap's pretty face this time. He ducked, which caused me to hit Spence instead. He looked at me bewildered, like he thought I had done it on purpose.

The willowy chap came for me, clawing at my face with his fingernails. He meant to do me all the damage he could, too—he had long fingernails, painted green—so I doubled up my fist and just whacked him one.

I caught him good, too, let me tell you. I might not be no bigger than a minute, as Papa always said, but I'm stronger than you'd think. It set him right down on his tight little ass, and I was ready to let him have the brother to that first lick as soon as he got to his feet. But he stayed down, starting to cry something awful, the mascara streaking down his cheeks until he looked a holy mess. Seeing that I had won out, all I could think about was getting away, so people wouldn't keep staring and making comments. So, taking Spence by the hand, I led him across the narrow street right through the automobile traffic.

Once on the other sidewalk, I stopped to catch my breath. "That's just about the durndest thing I

191

ever got into in my life," I said. I was still as mad as a hornet. "What made him want to do such a thing, I wonder?"

I noticed, then, that Spence was looking across the street to where the chap was standing now, wipping at his eyes with a lacy handkerchief. The people were moving on, the big show all over, so he was lost in the crowd, no longer the center of attention, even if he was crying.

"Come on," I said.

Spence didn't move. I jerked on his arm, making him move a step or two, but he was still looking over his shoulder.

"Listen," I said sharp-like. "If you want the chap, it's fine with me."

Spence gave me a look. Then he bowed his head to study his feet. "I've always wondered what it'd be like with a fellow," he said. "Ever since I first heard about it, couple of years ago."

I stared at him. "So the chap was right," I said. "He spotted you, didn't he?"

His voice got sullen. "Besides, he said it wouldn't cost nothing. I go with you, I ain't got but ten bucks left to get home on. I had it in mind to spend two nights in New Orleans on that kind of money." He braced himself up. "Why, it ain't been two hours since I got off the Greyhound bus."

It just flew all over me. "You don't have to explain," I said in a short voice. "Just go do your druthers, that's all."

With which remark, I walked to the curb and lifted one hand, beckoning to the willowy chap. He saw me and came across the street, still wary enough to stop ten feet away.

"What do you want?" he said, just as nasty as he could.

"He's all yours," I said. "You fellows have fun, hear?"

192

With that, I walked away.

I was so mad with the world, I had to walk the block three times before I could risk going back into Eddie's bar. If anybody had said a kindly word to me, I'd have bit his head off. But the longer I walked, the funnier it got, so that I started laughing inside, until finally I stopped and laughed out loud until my sides ached—and I made another spectacle of myself doing it.

So I came back to Eddie's bar in a real good humor. Eddie came, bringing me a Coke, and said, "Well. That was a quickie."

I laughed all over again. "It wasn't even a quickie. I lost him before I got two feet beyond that door yonder."

Eddie had to know all about it, so I told the story, making it even funnier than it had happened, Eddie laughing fit to bust a gut. Then I asked Eddie what the chap had meant, calling me a fish, and what the word "trade" meant, because when I hear something new, I like to find out about it. I don't believe in going through life ignorant; a person ought to learn something new every day if she can.

Before Eddie got through explaining, a stranger laid his arm around my shoulder, leaning over and saying, "I'd like to borrow your friend here, if I may. She's just the cutest little blond I've seen in a month of Sundays."

I looked around to see the biggest man I'd ever laid eyes on. It wasn't fat, either, but solid muscle. His head was so far up there you wouldn't believe it, making his face look terribly small, and he was as wide as he was tall, nearly. Tiny, which is what he was called, told me once he weighed exactly four hundred and two pounds, stripped naked, and he was a wrestler by trade.

So Tiny, instead of Spence, turned out to be my first New Orleans fellow, and big though he was, he

193

was just as nice and gentle a man as a girl could hope to meet. He became just about my most faithful friend, good for once a week like clockwork, and after we had got to know each other he always took a whole night of my time, which set him back a cool hundred and fifty. He could afford it, though, because he made big money at his trade.

He delighted to drink with me at his side, which didn't bother me, because he could put down more whiskey than any ten men and not show the first sign. One of his pleasures, whilst drinking and being sociable with his many friends, was to set me up on his arm, not even bracing it on the bar, and have me sit there like a banty hen on a roost for an hour at a time.

Tiny told me he'd always had trouble with women because of his size. It scared them off, seems like, before he could get a chance to let them know he was just an ordinary good old boy. Well, he *was* the biggest man ever crawled on top of little old me, but the funny part was, his old Thing was, if anything, sort of puny, if you know what I mean. Of course, I never told *him* that in so many words.

So I was off to a fine New Orleans start, and it kept getting better. I was making so much money that Eddie showed me how to open a savings account, as a safe place to keep my earnings, and extravagant though it was, I kept on living at the Holiday Inn. After a month or two, the bar where Eddie worked got to be almost like the artesian well back home; I'd walk in every night to greet my regular friends with a kiss, letting them know who was first tonight and who was last, and in between trips across the street we'd laugh and talk and have a good time. Most, I do believe, knew right well that I wasn't drinking nothing but iced tea, but they were proud to buy it for me.

I didn't know at the time how lucky I had been

194

to find Eddie right off the bat, didn't realize how much trouble he kept off my back. I didn't even know, at the time, that what I was doing was supposed to be against the law. Eddie had only told me I ought to be careful who I chose to go with, so that, when it was a stranger, I'd look at Eddie, to get either a nod or a shake of his head. It wasn't only that it might be a cop looking to run a girl in for practicing her natural trade; he warned me off men known to be weird in their ways, too.

So if it hadn't happened to be Eddie's night off, the bad thing wouldn't have happened—or maybe it would have, maybe there wasn't no way to dodge what was coming to me.

This new fellow come up to me that night. I was sort of uneasy about him right from the start, because he was the sharp sort of dresser that it didn't look like he'd have to buy It, but able to find plenty of silly girls willing to give It away. He was slim, with a dark, narrow face, and he wore this white coat and a real pretty hat, all pearl-colored, with a wide brim to it like a plantation hat, except it was too fancy to wear out working in the sun. He carried a smart cane, slim and pretty, and wore pointy shoes that you could see your face in, they sported such a shine.

But I did answer back when he spoke to me, because it was raining, the bar was practically empty, and I hadn't made a dime yet. Just one of those nights when none of my regular friends had come around, you see, nor any strangers.

He didn't make any bones about it, saying, "How much is It, sweetheart?"

I looked him over, seeing a thin mouth and sharp eyes, and told him.

"Let's go across the street," he said.

So he had already heard the good word about me, somewhere or other. It made me feel some better to know that.

195

We went outside, waited a few minutes under the awning—all the time him tapping his cane impatiently against the sidewalk—until the rain let up enough for us to hurry across the street. The fellow on the desk looked at my new friend; then he glanced at me, but he didn't say anything except "Five dollars," and turned away to his comic book. Which was strange; he generally had some remark, even if it wasn't always friendly.

Upstairs, my new friend looked around the room. "You're fixed very nice here."

Didn't many fellows notice it, but I had worked on my room. I always used the same one, you see, and because it had been dreary-looking to me, I had spent my own money to fix it up. First I bought a new carpet—the old one didn't have any color left, and puffed dust at every step. Then I had a fellow to paint the walls a bright lemon color, so nice and cheerful, and I had hung some pictures I had found in this funny little shop around the corner. I had even brought in a good bed, because the other had squeaked something awful. At fifty dollars a throw, I figured a fellow ought to have a nice place to do It in.

I was pleased that he had noticed. "Did it myself," I told him. "It is nice, ain't it?"

"Take off your clothes, let me look at you," he said.

He stood in the middle of the room, leaning on his cane, still wearing his pearl hat and coat and a tie with a diamond stickpin, bright and shiny, watching while I got naked. It made me sort of chill, the way his eyes were cold and narrow, and suddenly I found myself wishing that Eddie had been on duty to check this fellow out.

When I stood naked, he reached out his cane and turned me with it. "Nice," he said "Very nice."

"Lots of folks thing so," I said brightly, trying to be friendly.

"Yeah. That's what I've heard." He poked me with the cane again, turning me on around.

"Listen," I said, trying to laugh. "I don't like the way you handle me with that old stick of yours."

"What's to like, sweetheart?" he said. "I bought you, didn't I?"

My laugh sounded pretty nervous to my ears. "Ain't seen the color of your money yet."

Putting his hand in his pocket, he pulled out a roll of bills big enough to choke a jackass. Peeling off three twenties, he flung them on the bed.

"It ain't but fifty," I said.

"That's all right," he said. "Now, undress me."

He stood there in the middle of the room whilst piece by piece I took off his clothes. I did it with careful loving, too, thinking I ought to get It over with, I'd feel a lot safer in the bar. But even with sliding warm hands over his naked skin, and talking nice, I hadn't done him a bit of good.

He saw me looking at his limp old Thing, so he said, "You know what to do about it, don't you?"

Well, I'd done learned a long time ago that lots of fellows like a girl to use her sweet mouth on him; it's not that I mind it, as long as their old Thing is nice and clean. But it did turn me off, the way he hooked the handle of his walking stick around my neck and dragged me down on my knees.

I put my hands to him, all right, to let him know my heart was in the right place. But then I looked up into his face and told him, "You do that one more time, I'll bite it off for you."

He didn't say anything, so I went about my business; I just meant to let him know he couldn't have his way about everything.

He stood there without making a sound of pleasure, didn't put his hands on my head to push my mouth deeper onto him, didn't do anything a fellow usually does in a situation like that. But finally he got a little something to brag about, so he moved over to lie down on the bed, letting me know that he wanted me on top.

It turned out to be just about the most curious kind of fucking I'd ever done up to that time. He didn't do nothing to help out; just laid there, not even holding me with his arms or arching his hips to take the goodies, and let me work. His old Thing would get hard, then it'd turn soft again, at which time he'd shove me down to mouth him up some more.

It went on for the longest time; we were already well over the hour, but I had already made up my mind not to start an argument with this fellow, not if I could help it. So I didn't mention that he'd owe the desk clerk another five dollars; I just kept on doing what he showed me he wanted done.

He never did get to it. Not even close. It was finally that his old Thing just withered away for good and all, and taking me by the shoulders, he shoved me sprawling to the floor.

"Say, now, that ain't nice," I said.

He didn't reply, just started getting dressed. Except, when I picked up my dress, he told me to keep naked.

"It's over and done with," I said. "I'm going back to the bar. You'll owe the fellow on the desk another five dollars."

He finished knotting his tie and walked over to the closet. Opening it, he took out a coat hanger, with one jerk of his hands pulling it out into two straight pieces of wire.

"Now, wait a minute. I don't go in for that kind of stuff," I said.

He hit me before I could speak another word. The wire coat hanger stung my ass, and I just knew

198

it had made a welt. I squalled like a cat and started running. But, shoot, that fellow could move fast when he took a notion. Before I was halfway to the door, he had caught me, lifted me in one move, and flung me to the bed. Then, holding a pillow over my head to muffle my hollering, he went to work.

I had been spanked pretty good by Papa in my time. But it hadn't ever felt anything like this, because Papa had always used the flat of his hand on my bare bottom, and nearly always wound up drunk and crying for what he had done. This fellow was just as cold and mean as the devil about his whipping. He went at it like chopping wood, just whap, whap, whap, and no matter how I twisted or turned, he didn't hold back, striking wherever it happened to fall, front or back.

I hollered as loud as I could, which wasn't much, with my face mashed into the mattress and the pillow pressed down over my head. Then, for a while, I took to crying. That didn't relieve the situation either, so finally I laid there and took it, feeling my flesh jump and quiver with every burning lick. Didn't none of it make any difference; he didn't quit until he got through.

When he stood up and flung away the coat hanger, I sat up on the side of the bed to look at him. He hadn't even worked up a sweat. I wiped at my face with shaking hands, sore and shamed all over.

"Why did you have to do that?" I asked him. "I done you the best I could, given what I had to work with."

He showed me a tight smile. "Yes, sweetheart, you're as good as they told me you were. That was just a lesson to let you know that a little whore like you can't work my street behind my back."

"What *are* you talking about?"

"I'm Snake Dubois," he said. He watched me to see if I knew the name, but, shoot, I hadn't ever

199

heard it. "Every girl on this street works for me. Just like, from now on, you will, too."

"I don't work for nobody but myself."

He went over and picked up the coat hanger. "Let me hear you say that again, sweetheart."

I looked at the man. I knew him now. He could start in and whip me all over again, and enjoy every minute of it.

"Come on," he said urgently. "Say it again. I like beating on your sweet little ass."

"I ain't never worked for nobody but myself . . . up till now," I told him, my voice shaking with the words.

"That's more like it," he said. He went to pick up my purse, opened it, looked into it. "You mean to tell me I'm the first trick you've turned tonight?" he said, taking out his sixty dollars and putting it back on his roll.

"Yes," I said.

He was studying me again with his narrow eyes. "You're bone lazy," he said. "Just like all whores. When you work for me, I mean for you to hustle. Understand, sweetheart?"

"It's raining," I said. "It's a slow night."

"Five tricks, that's your quota," he said. "Any night you can't turn five, raining or not, I'm gonna beat your ass. Understand? I won't have you sitting on your tail in that bar having yourself a good time. I want you *hustling*. Hear me, sweetheart?"

"Yes, sir," I said. I just wanted to get out of there. I knew it wouldn't do any good to try to talk to this Snake Dubois. He was beyond talking.

It pleased him to hear me name him "sir," so he gave me the thin smile again. "That's more like it. I think we'll get along fine."

I stood up, stiff and sore and feeling like a hundred years old. Moving slowly, I started putting on my dress.

"Where do you think *you're* going?" he said.

I stopped. "I thought our business was over and done with for the time being."

"There's one other thing you've got to do for me."

I stood holding my dress in my hand, wondering, while he went out the door. In a few minutes he came back, with the desk clerk following. I stared at him so hard, this fellow's eyes darted here and yonder without looking at me.

"I promised my friend a piece on the house," Snake Dubois told me. "So you just lay down there and treat him as nice as you did me."

"I can't," I said. "I'm too sore."

The desk clerk, licking his lips nervously, looked to Snake Dubois.

"Lay down," Snake said to me.

I laid down. With the crook of his cane, Snake Dubois hooked one ankle and pulled my leg out. Then he hooked the other ankle and moved that leg, leaving me laid out open. He looked at the desk clerk.

"Jump and hump her, boy," he said. "Snake Dubois keeps his promises."

I said, "Mr. Snake, you say I'm working for you now. But right off the bat you're making me do something I ain't never done, and that's give It away."

I couldn't help but feel bad about taking that desk clerk's old Thing into me, with him not paying the first dollar to put it there. I hadn't ever been obliged to do It with somebody looking, either; Snake Dubois leaned on his cane and watched with his cold eyes like we were a couple of dogs going at It.

Well, I might be forced to give It away, but I want you to know, that desk-clerk fellow sure got a cold old me. Let him labor and snort and surge all he wanted to, he wasn't entitled to any of that sweet good stuff I knew so well how to put out that I reckon I was just born with knowing how. Which made him take a while, his old Thing realizing the cold reception even if he was too dumb to know it himself. I didn't shift an inch to help, even to get rid of him, but laid cold and still like I was being raped. Which I reckon I was, in a sort of a way.

When finally he was done, he felt so mean with himself that he had to remark, "I don't see what all the talk is up and down the street about this one. She's just another cold hunk of tail, as far as I'm concerned."

"That's all you wanted out of it when you put me on to her," Snake said icily. "Now you're complaining, sport?"

The fellow got nervous. "Sure, Snake, sure, it was just that, seeing her switch her tail up and down those stairs . . ." He took a deep breath and tried to laugh. "I guess I got it all built up in my head, when she ain't nothing but just another whore."

"You can brag that you got the first piece she ever gave away. You'll have to be satisfied with that."

The fellow left as fast as he could. Snake looked to me. "You really do hate to give It away, don't you, sweetheart?" he said, laughing for the first time.

"Can I go home now?" I said, not making a move toward getting dressed until I had his word.

He looked at his watch. "There's time to turn three more tricks before the night's done."

"Listen," I said. "I'm sore as a boil from that whipping. I can't . . ."

"I've told you once, sweetheart. When you work for me, you hustle. So get to it."

I hustled. While Snake Dubois sat at a back table in the bar, just the one drink in front of him all evening, I found three fellows to take across the street, one after the other. Every time I came back, Snake looked at me with those cold eyes, and *kept* watching me until I went out with the next one.

Knowing he was there made me sort of frantic. I hadn't ever felt like I'd needed to push It. But I found myself cajoling and making promises like never before. I had always stood on my record, knowing that I was just the best piece of ass a man could hope to buy. But I didn't have my confidence after that whipping; every time I missed out and had to seek out another fellow, I could just feel that mean coat hanger whistling against my sore ass.

When I came into the bar after the third trick, Snake lifted his cane, beckoning. I went to stand before him. Taking my purse out of my hand, he opened it and found the hundred and fifty dollars. With great care he wrapped it around his roll and put it all back into his pocket.

"Don't I get to keep any at all?" I said.

He glanced up as if it surprised him I was still there. "Sweetheart, you've been working my street so long without paying me my share, I figure you owe me. You'll get cut in when I decide you've caught up your debts."

There wasn't anything else to do but take my aching body home to the Holiday Inn. But tired as I was, hurting though I was, I laid awake for the longest time, my head just spinning with hurt and shame and despair. The world can change so fast, sometimes, on a girl, she can't hardly know what to do.

The next morning wasn't any better. I woke up welted all up and down my backside, and even on the fronts of my legs, where he had caught me twisting. I had thought he was whipping me to blood, but he knew exactly how to use that coat hanger, hard enough to hurt but not to draw blood. After all, I was now his property; he wouldn't want to cause permanent damage.

I had always felt so good, getting dressed in the early part of the evening to go to work. As I had carried that good feeling out into the street, the lights were beginning to flash brighter with the going of the sun, people shaping themselves up for another exciting New Orleans night. Me, too, thinking about all my friends waiting, anxious to enjoy the use of my body the way it had been built to be enjoyed, and just knowing I was having fun and doing good in the world at the same time.

But now, with Snake Dubois taking charge of my life, you'd have thought I was going to pick cotton, the way I walked sad and heavy-footed, to stand outside the bar before I could screw up my nerve to enter.

Sure enough, this second night, there was Snake sitting at his back table. Eddie, I was glad to see, was behind the bar; I had hoped he'd come around today, so I could talk to him, but he hadn't.

Five tricks, I told myself. Then it'll be over for one night, anyway.

So I set to work. For good luck, it was easy, because tonight was a Saturday, and lots of friends had come to see me. I lined up five, one after the other, and in the interest of getting through as quick as possible, I told them to come on across the street as soon as the fellow ahead got back to the bar.

I hadn't ever hustled my friends so hard; we'd always sat in the bar, in between, and had ourselves a good time. But all I wanted was to get it over with; and though it puzzled them to see me change my ways, they agreed to it. So I went out with the first customer and started sharecropping.

It wasn't more than a couple of hours before I could come back across the street and face Snake Dubois, knowing I had filled my quota. Because I

204

had the money in my purse, I sat down at the table instead of standing before him.

I took the bills out of my purse and handed them over. "There it is," I said. "Five tricks. Just like you said."

He smiled. "That's a good girl," he said. "You learn fast, don't you, sweetheart?"

"I wasn't standing behind the door when they passed out good sense," I said. I got up. "I'll be seeing you."

"Wait a minute," he said.

I turned around.

"Five tricks, that's the bottom line," he said. "I didn't say that was *all* you had to do. It's just enough to keep your ass from getting beat again."

He sure knew how to take the heart out of a girl. "What's the *all* I have to do?"

"All you can," he said. "What else? You quit work when the street closes, not a minute before. Understand?"

"You're a hard man," I said.

He smiled his thin smile. "I'm a nice man, sweetheart. If you'll let me be."

"What is all this?" Eddie said.

I turned to look at him standing beside me. He'd seen me give Snake the money, I reckon.

"What business is it of yours, sport?" Snake asked politely.

"Listen, this girl is my friend," Eddie said.

Snake's eyes got narrow and hard. "You're Eddie the bartender. Right?"

"Yeah, that's right."

"So you're the sport who's been running this girl on my street," Snake said. "Eddie, I've been thinking about you."

It must have been that Eddie hadn't taken a good look at the man before. He moved a step back. "I ain't running no girls," he said. "I wouldn't do that,

that's not my line of work. We're just friends, that's all."

Snake sneered at him. "I suppose you're not taking money from her."

"Not a thin dime," Eddie said hotly.

"That's the truth," I said.

Snake looked at me. Then he looked at Eddie again. "She's my girl now," he said flatly. "She's working for me." He looked at me. "Isn't that right, sweetheart?"

I could just see that coat hanger showing in his hand if I said the wrong thing. Besides, there was Eddie to think about.

"Yes, Eddie," I said. "I'm working for him now."

Snake smiled. "See, sport? A nice girl like her needs somebody to look after her. Which I am now doing. So you'd better just get behind the bar and tend to your own business. All right?"

Eddie went away. Snake turned again to me. "You'd better get hustling, sweetheart. You're wasting time, standing here talking."

With a heavy heart I started in all over again, hurrying them along, doing those things I had always done just for nice, with nothing in my head but the idea of milking it out of their old Things quick, and get on to the next john. I guess I figured that if I could do enough to please Snake Dubois, he'd take his weight off my back. But I should have known; no woman in the world could have hustled hard enough to satisfy Snake Dubois's greed. Because it wasn't just money; he had to lean on a girl at the same time, no matter how much cold hard cash she put into his pocket. That was just the way he was.

I didn't have the chance to talk to Eddie until the night was almost over. Finally, seeing Snake go to the pay phone, I whispered across the bar, "I've got to talk to you, Eddie. Can you meet me outside when the bar closes?"

206

"Sure," Eddie said. He glanced toward the back of the room. "Who is that guy, anyway?"

"Name's Snake Dubois," I said. "That's all I know."

Eddie's face went pale. "Snake Dubois," he said. "Oh, my God."

Seeing Snake returning to his table, I had to leave Eddie without another word. But when the bar closed, I found out why Eddie was so scared. I had paid Snake the money for the six new tricks I had turned, not even getting a thank you, and went outside to wait for my friend. He finally came hurrying out of the alley that ran beside the bar.

"Listen," he said, "I can't talk now. I've got to—"

I grabbed Eddie by the arm. "What's the matter? I've got to tell—"

He shook my hand loose. Jerky in his movements, he was looking up and down the street.

"Listen, if you're working for Snake Dubois, I don't want to have anything to do with you," he said roughly. "Understand?"

"Ed-die . . ." a voice called.

We whirled around. Down the empty street—it's amazing how quick it can clear out once the bars close; all I could see was one fellow walking down the other side toting a trumpet case—there stood Snake Dubois. Two fellows were with him.

"Come here, sport," Snake said, his voice carrying in the night air.

Eddie didn't want to. But he went, and I went with him. When he stood before Snake, he said, "Listen, Snake. I don't want any trouble."

"But you've got trouble, sport," Snake said. He took a step to one side. "All right, fellows. He's all yours."

I knew what was going to happen. I set myself to charge in to help Eddie, even though he was just standing there, his hands hanging, his head down.

207

But I didn't have a chance. Snake laid his walking stick across my chest, which was all he needed to do to hold me.

"You'd better go home and get your beauty sleep, sweetheart," Snake said. "You'll need it tomorrow night."

I looked at Eddie. He wouldn't look at me. "Don't hurt him," I said. "He didn't do nothing."

Snake pressed the cane harder against my chest. "Go home," he said. "Like I told you."

I went. Because there wasn't anything else a girl could do. I even hurried, so I wouldn't hear the sounds that Eddie would start making when they took to hitting on him.

I never saw Eddie again. He just didn't come back to work after that night. So all I had left in the world was Snake Dubois, and being Snake Dubois's girl.

It took all the suption out of my life. This Snake Dubois had the talent of making you feel like a slave must have felt in the olden times; it wasn't just that you knew he'd beat on you, or that his eyes were as cold as his heart. It was something so far beyond, I can't even begin to describe it.

Now, an independent-minded girl like me, you'd have thought that I would have packed my bag, found the nearest truck stop, and rode out of that town. God knows, I thought about it. But I couldn't seem to hoist myself up enough to make the move. It wasn't just that I'd be going back to work for a dollar a whack, when I'd got used to fifty dollars for exactly the same doings. Somehow, it just didn't seem possible to walk away from a man like Snake Dubois; I had the feeling, deep down in my gut, that somehow, somewhere, someway, he'd find me. Then I would catch it in ways I hadn't dreamed of yet. He had that effect on a person.

But, most of all, it was that the spirit, which had

brought me all this long road from working for a quarter a piece down there at the artesian well, seemed to be gone out of me. All I could hold in my head was how to please Snake by hustling hard enough and long enough. All I could think about was getting done with this one and finding one or two or three more before the night was out. I used all my sweet little habits, that had ever pleasured mankind, not to make them feel good but simply to get rid of them as quick as possible. Which ain't the way any girl, getting paid or not, ought to do. So—and I suppose Snake knew this, too, how to bring it about—I had to feel cheap about myself, knowing I was a sorry lay when all my life I had taken pride in counting myself just the greatest girl that ever took off her pants.

So Snake Dubois really and truly owned me; he had made me his slave. Because he had changed my outlook on life, my opinion of myself.

I didn't have anybody to turn to. After Eddie was gone, I thought about my big man; he was so liked, so respected, and if Snake wanted to beat up on him, he'd better bring along about a dozen useful fellows to do it with. So I talked to Tiny. But he wouldn't have any part of it, saying, "Girl, you can't expect me to go up against Snake Dubois."

"But you're the biggest, strongest man I've ever seen."

He shook his head. "Ain't a matter of muscle strength. Why, if I looked crosseyed at Snake Dubois, I wouldn't wrestle in this town again. He's got power in ways me and you don't even know about, honey."

So that was that.

After the first week, Snake quit watching me so close, though he showed every night to collect the money. He hadn't let me keep a dollar yet, either, so that I was having to use up my savings for the privilege of working for him. So it was that, since he couldn't have seen how many fellows I had taken, I held out a trick on him.

When I handed over the night's earnings, he looked at the money and said, "You're fifty dollars short."

I started to tremble. "How did you know?"

He smiled his thin smile. "I'm not dumb, sweetheart. I knew it was the next thing you'd think up."

Without a further word, I gave him the fifty. But then I said, "You can't expect a girl to work forever without earning a dime. I've got to live too, you know."

Like it was nothing, he fingered a ten-dollar bill loose from his roll and tossed it to me. "Here. Go buy yourself something pretty."

I looked at the bill. Here I was in the hole again, making less than a dollar a man. Tonight I had done thirteen. But there wasn't nothing to say. There never was.

It wasn't just the money, it was Snake Dubois, too. About once a week, he'd show up at the Holiday Inn with a doctor in tow. At least, he was a fellow who carried a black bag, though he was so slick and greasy, and sly of hand, that I wouldn't have let him doctor a sick cat. After he had examined me for disease, and had left, I had to take off Snake Dubois's clothes and give him a piece of It.

If you could call the way he did getting a piece. I'm ashamed to admit it, but I never did manage to make that fellow come to the point. He's the only man I've ever had to say that about. But, Lord, he was as cold as ice, he'd just lay there and let me work away until I'd think for sure this time I'd break him down —and I wanted to, because I had the idea that if just once I could make him come, it might cause him to be kinder in his nature.

So I gave Snake the best of everything, but all to no use. He liked a girl to be a slave, so I did them eagerly, all the slave things I don't like to think about even now. But as far as I could tell, it didn't make a dime's worth of difference in his feelings. I'd love him and love him and keep on loving him, and when he'd had enough he'd fling me off to the floor and go get a coat hanger.

I really do believe, come to think about it, he he took more real hard-down pleasure out of beating on me than from all the fine things I did for him. But what hurt my feelings more than the weekly whippings hurt my body was that he'd make me give It away from time to time.

He'd hand me a card with an address on it and tell me to go there. Often it was a big house or a fancy French Quarter apartment, sometimes a hotel suite or a private men's club somewhere out on the lake. These men were different from any I had ever known, older generally, and pretty set in their ways. Big men, I could tell, used to power and money and getting free goodies like me from those who wanted to curry their favor. But when they took off their pants, often they had nothing but trouble getting their old Things up. And then blamed it on the girl.

It made some of them strange in their ways, let me tell you. One old fellow wanted me to walk all over him in high-heeled shoes, and another, who I saw pretty regular, just wanted me to throw oranges at him. It really turned him on, too. Sometimes it'd turn out to be a party, with other girls there and everybody doing It right out in the open. I never did like that, because after all, a girl is entitled to her privacy, ain't she?

Being so brought down to the nothing of myself, and knowing it every waking minute of my life, I reckon I would have stayed a slave to Snake Dubois till yet if it hadn't been that I took to wandering around the French Quarter in the afternoons. I suppose I did it because, Snake having taken the rest of

211

my life, I had to find a little something for myself. So I'd get up about two o'clock, and after dressing myself just as careful, go strolling up and down the streets looking into the shops and watching the people. New Orleans is a town for all sorts; I could study the passersby and wonder what kind of lives they were leading, and for an hour or two get outside of myself. Which was good, because I didn't like myself much anymore.

One afternoon, I noticed this woman following me. Every time I turned a corner, she'd turn the corner right behind me. It made my heart sore to realize that Snake Dubois had me staked out, even in this free time, and so knew all that I was doing.

I went along until I came to Jackson Square, where I sat down on a bench. After a minute she sat down beside me. So I just turned and looked her up and down. An old woman, thin and tall, with these glasses down on her nose like Ben Franklin used to wear, tied to her dress with a black ribbon in case they happened to fall off.

"What do *you* want?" I said.

She looked at me, sort of smiling. "What makes you think I want anything?"

"You've been following me long enough," I said.

She kept on smiling. "You're one of Snake Dubois's girls, aren't you?"

"You ought to know," I said. "You work for him too, don't you?" I looked her over, feeling mean. "But not in the same way, I don't think."

She laughed. "No. I don't work for Snake. But I know him." She paused, watching me. "A fellow named Eddie told me about you."

It perked up my interest. "How is Eddie, anyway?"

"He decided to leave town for his health," she said dryly. "Went to Miami, I think."

"Is he all right?" I said urgently. "Eddie was just the finest fellow in the world."

"He won't ever be as handsome as he was," she told me. "But he's all right."

"What did Eddie tell you about me?" I asked, going back to her first statement that had caught my interest.

She looked me over again. "He asked me to do what I could for you."

I felt my shoulders slump. "Can't nobody help. That mean old Snake . . ."

"*I* can," she said.

I didn't believe her. "How?"

She did seem to smile a lot. "I have this house, where lots of girls stay with me," she said. "A very nice house—you'd like it there. And if you wish, you may come to my house."

"But Snake Dubois . . ."

"Don't worry about him. I'll take care of Snake Dubois." She was fumbling in her bag. "Here's my card. Get your clothes and come along as quickly as you can."

I took the card. "Why are you doing this? Just because Eddie . . ."

She chuckled. "Partly. But mostly because people whose judgment I trust tell me you're the greatest whore to ever hit this town. Since I run the best house in New Orleans, it's not entirely out of the kindness of my heart."

I looked at her again. It had been a long time since I had been able to like anybody. *Or* trust them.

So that was how it was that I came to the house called the Captain's Paradise.

The Boy

I want to tell you, I was the star of that sex show right from the start. They didn't have a man who could hold a candle to Him—though I must say, that jackass did himself right proud, and the white German shepherd dog was something else.

Here's how the show went. It took place in this large-sized room, furnished with sofas and love seats, all done up in red plush, for the audience; there was a little stage, curtain and everything, but not much on the stage except some pillows and bolsters, and one big workbench of a sofa—except, for the first act, there was this pole painted gold right out in the center that looked like a you-know-what.

The audience, mainly, was made up of men customers and the house girls who didn't take part in the show. The surprising thing, though, was that lots of women came, and they seemed to take a deal more interest than the men. Sometimes they'd get real worked up.

The first act, the curtains would open to show this lovely girl, dressed all in white, tied to the pole. Really tied, too, it looked like, with all these ropes and things, and her slumped down, her head hanging, the very picture of despair. Except that, with that white dress clinging to her, you could see everything she had; how they did that was, they made the dress wet before she went out to get tied up, so it would cling to her body.

She held the pose for a minute or two—the right kind of music, sad and low, yet with a beat, coming from the three-man combo. Then, showing every sign of fear, she'd jerk her head up and get tight in the body—you could *really* see everything, then—and here he would come.

The whip man wore a black suit, a tuxedo, you understand, and he'd be smoking a long, thin cigar. In each hand he held a whip, and all of a sudden he cracked both whips at the same time, making everybody jump. At this the girl went crazy with fear, struggling to escape from her bonds. He would only smile evilly and walk closer, starting the whips to cracking and curling around her body until you expected to see blood. But, shoot, being a real whip man, he never hurt her the least bit, though many and many a time a woman in the audience would start screaming, thinking he was lashing her to death.

After whipping her until she stood with head hanging, letting him have his way, he laid aside his cigar and went to work on them ropes, the whips cutting them loose one by one. Once free, of course, she got the idea of escaping, so she'd start running. Busy with lighting his cigar—oh, he was a haughty man, I tell you—he didn't seem to take notice until, at the last minute, one whip snaked out, lapped her

215

waist, and pulled her back into his arms. Holding her, one hand on her pussy and the other arm behind her back, he grinned at her while she lay with her head back in defeat, knowing now there wasn't no getting away.

Next, then, she went down to her knees to throw her arms around his hips, begging for mercy. No mercy from him; instead, he backed off, motioning her to stand up. When she did, showing hopelessness again, he went to work with both whips, snapping and lashing—and cut every stitch of that dress off her body, piece by piece! You could just feel the audience taking the liveliest interest. The last thing, she wore this little silver triangle between her legs, which he flicked out with the cracker of the whip just as neat as you please, at which she screamed like he had struck her to the quick.

The scream stirred him up, as well as the audience. Using one whip again, he lapped it around her legs and jerked her down onto these cushions on the floor. He snapped the whip around one ankle to pull that leg out. Then he snapped it around the other ankle. And there she lay, open for all to see.

And then . . . well, it was downright strange how this part got to the audience. Because, you see, the handle of one of his whips was shaped like unto a cock, and while she laid helpless he put that handle down there between her legs and shoved it up her.

Oh, she twisted and turned like it was killing her. But then, as he kept working it in clever ways, she was arching and squirming because it felt so good, her head back, her mouth open, and it was just the best piece of acting a body ever saw.

When he took it away, she laid there, her breasts heaving, her arms and legs in the air, begging for more. That was when he took out his own cock.

Now, this fellow wasn't what you'd call exactly built for the job. After all, he was a whip man, not a cock man, and in that way he was no more than ordinary. So he had this fake thing that popped out of his fly in the one moment he was turned away from the audience, and from the distance you couldn't tell it from the real thing. It was made out of this sort of material, you see, that looked like flesh, and it was shaped just right, and stood up stiff.

When he turned back, the phony cock brought a gasp from the audience, because it was so much bigger than you'd think a man could be. Standing backstage watching, I couldn't feel that it was hardly fair to have to follow a fake like that.

He turned her on her belly, using the whip, of course; then, kneeling, he shoved that huge thing into her from the back, making her scream again. But when he got to fucking, she liked it again, twisting and hollering and carrying on until she was going absolutely wild. When he was done with her, she crawled after him, begging for more, more, more, putting her hands all over that fake thing, and then her mouth, while he stood calmly lighting a fresh cigar.

Finally, bored with her, he shoved her away with one foot. She went sprawling, but came crawling back. He had his whips out, and now it was him holding her off as he backed off the stage, that great thing wagging and jerking as he moved, and him snapping and cracking the whips, keeping her off like a lion tamer gets away from that old ferocious lion. When he finally escaped, she lay there on the floor, naked and crying and pumping her hips in the need, until the curtains hid her from view.

The curtains, opening again, showed this big blond woman laying on the sofa doing it to herself with her hand. She had on this red dressing gown, so sheer you could see through it, but shoot, nothing was covered up, she was sprawled out so. It went on like that for some time until she was satisfied, and smiling, pulled the red gown over her hips and went to sleep.

217

In just a minute, this big white German shepherd dog trotted onto the stage.

Now, this was the blond lady's very own pet, and she had him trained in ways you wouldn't believe. First, seeing her laying there, he stopped to take a look, his head cocked to one side. Then, getting down on his belly, he sneaked up on her and with his teeth took hold of that red dressing gown and pulled it off, leaving her naked. She stirred at that, seeming about to wake up. He waited until she had settled down. When she did, she wound up with her legs laying wide open.

Which caused him to jump up on the sofa and sniff at her cunt. There was a comedy thing here, where he raised his head high, baring his upper lip, making the audience laugh. But when he put his head between her legs and started licking her, they quit laughing and started watching again, tense and quiet.

It was like at first the blond lady was having a nice dream. It must have felt good, really and truly, anyway, as she arched her pussy to take the dog's tongue. How I know is, after I'd been there a while I found out that he got to do his tricks, often and often, without waiting for show time; not only with the blond lady, but also with her friends amongst the girls of the house.

I want to tell you, that dog did enjoy his stardom. He just crouched down there and brought her to the wild point. When she woke up, she laid staring at the dog, a horrified expression on her face. Then she kicked him off the sofa and shook her finger at him, naughty, naughty, so that he put his nose down between his paws, acting ashamed of himself. Which made the audience laugh all over again.

So she lit a cigarette, and sighed and stretched, and after a minute that dog looked up and wagged

218

his tail. She forgave him, of course, and he came to have his ears scratched. Well, that only encouraged him, because suddenly he wrapped both front legs around her leg and started hunching, his cock showing red and dripping.

She pushed him away. He came back. She pushed him away again. He came back, hunching at her, and laughing at her with his open mouth, because he was sure of himself now, she hadn't pushed so hard this last time. She looked at him for a long minute. Then, sliding halfway off the sofa, she caught that dog under the front legs and pulled him to her. Reaching down, she guided his cock into her pussy, and then he just fucked her to a fare-thee-well until he came in her. That act was a real favorite of the show.

Next, three girls came out, one a black girl and one a blond and the other a redhead, and they did the strangest things to each other, twisting and turning and lapping and sucking in such a tangled heap that it was hard to keep up with who was doing what to who. After they had finished, three fellows came out and did the same thing, except, it being man-to-man this time, they couldn't practice as many different positions as the girls. They put their heart into their work, though, because I do think it was the part of the show they most enjoyed.

Next came the turn of the donkey. Not much showmanship to this act, just the plain, blunt fact. The curtain opened to show this woman laying on a sort of rack that opened her wide to view. Now, she wasn't very young or very pretty; with what she did, I reckon she didn't have to be. Because, as she laid there on that trestle thing, two girls led out the donkey. The woman started stroking his piece with her hand, so that it came to a stand. Now, I want to tell you! That jackass could make a fellow want to go home and raise chickens. You wouldn't believe how long and strong it did get.

When he was ready, the girls swiveled the trestle around, getting the woman under his belly, and then jacked it up so she could reach that great cock. She took it inch by inch, while showing every sign of enjoying the experience. And maybe she did, I don't know, but I don't hardly see how. While it disappeared in her inch by inch, the audience gasped and murmured, especially the female visitors.

I want you to know, once it was buried, she started moving, actually fucking that dumb animal, while he stood with his ears laid back, until he got excited, too, and started driving it at her, so that you wondered he didn't split her right up the middle.

When the applause started, real appreciation, the old lady would turn her head to smile out at the audience. As long as they clapped, she kept fucking, and when she got out from under the donkey she actually skipped out and took a bow.

Intermission time now, a chance to have a drink and talk about what they had seen, whilst another talented lady moved among them, picking up half-dollars in the strangest way you ever heard of; she could reach right out there and grab that money with her cunt. It was something to see, all right. She didn't give back the half-dollars, either.

After the intermission came my star turn. First, the lady who owned the house got up to make a little speech. This is what she said:

"Ladies and gentlemen, the Captain's Paradise is proud to bring to you tonight a very special attraction. You will now have the opportunity to view, in still life and in action, what I must call, in all modesty, the greatest cock in the world. It is my pleasure to tell you that the fucking tool you will see here tonight has been immortalized in the greatest

220

sculpture of modern times, now on view in the Museum of Modern Art in New York City."

I didn't know it to be actually so; Miss Ruby had told Miss Bascom about Charlotte Ainsley's work, but I had no idea where it had gone to after the New York show. Miss Bascom, though, said it didn't matter, it was just that everybody knew about the Museum of Modern Art, so that was the place to say it was being exhibited.

Next she held up one of the clay models, which she had bought when the *Liberated Lady* and all her contents had been auctioned off, holding it before her in both hands.

"This, ladies and gentlemen, is a working model the world-famous artist made in preparation for creating her masterpiece. It is, as you can see, indeed a master piece."

The audience laughed. She stroked the model until they had settled down. Then, turning toward the closed curtain, she pointed dramatically. "Now, by special arrangement, the Captain's Paradise presents the real thing—the master cock of the world!"

At which the curtains opened, to show me raised up on a pedestal, all the girls in the show clustered stark naked below me, their arms lifted to worship Him. A spotlight focused on me, while in the background came the soft roll of drums.

Except there came a sigh of disappointment. I was fully clothed, you see, wearing a one-piece silver suit that fitted my body, neck to ankles, like a snake's skin fits a snake.

No time for the disappointment to last, though, because, the drums rolling stronger and louder, the girls reached up to take hold of the legs and tear the silver suit from my body. It was made especially to break away, leaving me naked.

The drums stopped. Dead silence as they

gazed upon Him. He never failed to rise to the occasion, either, because if any one thing pleased Him, it was to be appreciated and acclaimed.

The silence that greeted Him as He came to a stand was better than any applause. It was at this time, as I had been told to do by Miss Bascom, that I looked boldly at every visiting lady in the house, one by one. It was something wonderful to see their expressions, too; some there were who covered their eyes and couldn't look—except they'd peek between their fingers; others were as bold as brass in showing their feelings; while a few got this secret, dreamy look to their faces.

The men were fun to watch. Not knowing how to act on viewing such a cock as they could never hope to have, some laughed nervously, some got a sneer on their faces and leaned to make an unfriendly remark to their nearest companion. Some, of course, were honest enough to show real appreciation and admiration.

Next, I turned sideways to show Him in profile, standing at His proudest. This move always brought the clap of hands, a rising ovation, in answer to which He would jerk and rise and get redder and harder than ever. The girls kneeling at the base of the pedestal started clamoring for Him then, some jumping up trying to touch Him, others laying down on the floor and moving their hips, trying to entice Him. I would then walk slowly down the steps on the back side of the pedestal and come forward on the stage. The girls knelt around me, some clinging to my legs, begging to feel Him in their pussy. Pointing my finger, I chose one girl to take Him reverently into her mouth, while the others caressed my body.

When she had got my hips to moving—I didn't fake it, either, but waited until He was feeling it, because I figured that whip fellow was fake enough for any one show—I pointed to the next girl. She would lay down on her belly, some pillows holding her ass up and ready, and I would ease Him into her and fuck her something good, while she screamed and hollered and carried on.

One by one He made good use of those girls, each in a different way. There were always four or five, sometimes six, and each just went wild when it came her turn. Of course, they *were* acting, being ladies of the house, and so, used to such doings; but sometimes I could tell it wasn't *all* acting by any manner or means.

After having gone through them all, He would have come down in size, so then I needed a girl to perk Him up with hand and mouth. Ready again, I laid down on the cushions and made the girls mount Him again one by one, fucking Him to a fare-thee-well and then some.

This last part, the girls pegged on top of Him, started the grand finale, bringing the entire cast —with the exception of the mule—out to take part in a general orgy, naked bodies all over the stage, while the musicians went into a jungle beat and different-colored lights started flickering over all that naked flesh arranged in strange and exciting combinations. There were men on men, women on women; two of the girls could take two cocks at once, one in cunt and the other in ass. The German shepherd, paws clasped around the waist of his mistress, was doing it dog fashion, which was his natural pleasure. There was also a billy goat doing the same thing to a girl. He was supposed to have a feature act of his own, but the girl hadn't got him trained up yet to be reliable; sometimes you couldn't get him interested, at other times he became so high-strung he'd just about tear that girl up. Or maybe he'd decide he liked another girl better, and chase *her* all over the place. The other girls didn't want any part of him, because, more than once, he had been known to hurt

223

the girl that trained him, to the point that she'd be bleeding by the time he got done. She wouldn't give up on the billy goat, though, because she wanted her stardom, if she could just manage to work it out.

Often, people from the audience would come down onstage to take part. The funny thing was, though once in a while a couple of men would get carried away, most often it was the ladies. They'd fuck in wilder ways than the working girls, too, once they let themselves go. Many was the time, as I laid there letting Him get fucked, I'd look up to see a visiting lady taking advantage of the situation.

The sex show was put on every Saturday night without fail, and often during the week for a special convention or something. I was paid one hundred dollars for each and every performance. Since, at best, there were never more than three performances a week, and not often that, the money wasn't hardly enough for a fellow to live on in an expensive town like New Orleans.

Miss Bascom, however, took care of that problem. First, she found me a real nice room not far from the Captain's Paradise; then she fixed it so I could take my meals in her kitchen along with the girls. Then she scrounged around and got me a job posing for pictures.

It was an interesting line of work. After I had signed up with this agency, they'd send me to these photographers' studios to pose wearing fine clothes or drinking beer or something like that. Of course, it was the girl who was nearly always the star attraction, with me standing around in the background somewhere, gazing longingly upon her sexiness. But, shoot, it was fifteen dollars an hour, which is good wages at just about anything, so I didn't care. I knew where *I* was the star, and that was good enough for me.

Of course, the work wasn't all that regular. But

pretty soon I had another string to my bow. The very first week I appeared in the sex show, a chauffeur fellow came upstairs to knock on my door one day and tell me his lady wished to speak to me. I went down to the car, and it wound up that she took me home with her for the night, for which she gave me just the prettiest pair of cufflinks you ever did see.

So I had my old ladies again. Miss Bascom made the suggestion that I ought to put in a telephone, being such a star attraction, so I did, and hardly a day went by that I didn't get called. Of course, I wouldn't see anybody the night before a performance, because I didn't want to run the risk of cutting down on His great act. A body has to give up a lot to be a star, let me tell you.

It *was* nice to have my old ladies again; I hadn't realized how much I'd missed them. It made me feel good to do somebody good again, and I found out that the rough road I had traveled in these last months hadn't spoiled me in knowing how they liked it, whether rough or smooth, sassy or gentle. Seems like every woman's got a picture in the back of her head how she wants a man to be, and I could read that picture just as plain.

So it looked like I had come out of the bad time for good and all. I still grieved for Miss Ruby, and guessed I always would; just like, in a different way, I grieved for Billy, my twin brother who had died of a fever when me and him were nine years old. But it was a distant sort of sadness, though that don't say it exactly the way I mean it.

As a matter of fact, when I glanced back over my adventures, it seemed like my whole life was far from me. I couldn't hardly remember the days of delivering groceries and kindnesses to my old ladies in Pass Robin. Having come such a long way, with so much happening to me, in spite of all trying I just

225

couldn't be anymore the young fellow that had started out so bright in life. I couldn't forget that, during the bad time, I had sunk so low as to take cash money from the gay boys of New Orleans. So I couldn't rear back on my hind legs anymore and say out loud, "I ain't no stud, and don't ever aim to be one." I had found out what a fellow will do when he sinks low. I reckon it's just the way of life to cause a man to do just exactly that one thing he says he won't do. It's a revenge on you, I do believe, for saying it . . . for thinking it . . . for feeling it.

There ain't but one thing for it: put the bad time behind you, don't keep looking back, but keep your face toward tomorrow. It may be good, and it may be bad, but you ain't lived it till yet, and so you've still got it to get through, while yesterday is gone and done with forevermore.

So I can't say that I had discontent in my soul to cause the next thing to happen. I didn't invite it by being dissatisfied with my life, and so it come on me like a piece of nature, a thunderstorm, say, building up and building up until it's just got to rain itself out regardless of what harm or what good it might do to the places and the people where it's got to happen, so the sky can be left smooth and calm again.

This was the way of it.

On this particular Saturday night, a new girl took part in the sex show. I happened to notice her because, as we waited backstage for the curtain to go up, she was still arguing with Miss Bascom that she didn't feel called on to perform, being as she had already proved herself the most popular girl in the house.

Miss Bascom wouldn't pay her any mind, just saying, "Love, when you work at the Captain's Paradise, you do what must be done. I didn't want to use you in the show, either, but three girls are out tonight; one's got her period, and one's got the disease—I'm

226

getting rid of that bitch, let me tell you, I run a clean place here—and the other girl had to go home to bury her mother."

She *was* a pretty thing, all blond and with the prettiest blue eyes you ever did see, and no bigger than a minute. Tiny though she was, she had a figure, just the nicest breasts and legs, and I liked the way she carried her mouth, mad though she was at the moment. Of course, I ain't never been much for young girls, as I have told, so I didn't try to get acquainted in any way; I don't hardly ever seem to have anything to say to a girl of that young nature.

Finally, over her own dead body, she went on in the sex show, and did her part right well. It so happened that, when it come to the star turn, I stood on the pedestal looking down on her as she reached up to plead for Him to come down and do her some good, like the acting called for. There was this bright look to her, so innocent and so pretty, that I just liked to look at her.

So when I came down off the pedestal to let the first girl love Him up with her mouth, I made up my mind I'd let her have the next part. So, when I pointed to her, she laid down on her belly, ready for me, and getting behind her, I rammed Him up into her pussy, solid and tight. When I did that, she looked around, smiling, and said, "Well, hello."

Which meant, I took it, that she liked the feel of Him. So I gave it to her good, thinking to pleasure her particularly since she hadn't wanted to take part at all, and it was then that the durndest thing happened.

Now, I have put Him into a good number of pussies in our time together, and most have been pretty nice places in which to find Himself. But I want to tell you here and now, hadn't *none* of my old ladies ever felt like unto this girl.

Why, it was *alive* in there, hot and ready and

227

just crawling all over Him, loving Him to death. Her pussy knew what He liked, and how to give it to Him. Why, it just pumped and sucked and surged all of its own, her not having to move her hips to do it, either, so that I was going at it, she was going at it, and we were just the best and truest friends in the world.

It went right out of my mind that I had the rest of the show to worry about. Only at the very last minute did I realize there was yet a lot of fucking to come, so that I had to stop dead cold to keep from losing the champion stuff then and there.

Even that didn't help much. Because she didn't quit when I did, and there I was, hanging on by the skin of my teeth, so that I just had to jerk Him out of that trap or find myself a defeated man. I had to grit my teeth to make myself do it, too. But I *was* the star, I had to remember that, and so I took Him away from her just in the nick of time.

Feeling Him leave, she turned to look into my face, and there was that in her eyes which let me know she understood damn well the danger she had put Him through. For a second, I was sure that she was laughing at me, because, feeling so downright mean about having to be in the show at all, she had set out to ruin my act. But, still looking at her, I realized that wasn't it at all; it was just the way she was. She couldn't help it no more than I could help pleasuring my old ladies.

So we smiled, each taking note of the quality discovered in the other, and went on with the show.

Now, it happened that often the performers would talk during the performance, in a low voice without moving the lips, so the audience couldn't hear. Most often, it was a remark about somebody in the audience; like one of the girls would say, "Look at that old fool in the front row, playing pocket pool with himself," and somebody else would say wisely, "Well, just think of the money he's saving." Or a girl

228

would tell me, "See that fat lady up there in the fur coat? Bet you a dollar she'll be down here on top of you the minute audience participation starts. She's been dying since she got the first look at your fancy cock."

As we began shaping up toward the general orgy, the new girl took an opportunity to whisper, "I've seen you somewhere. I know I have."

"I don't know where that could be," I said.

We got took away from each other, but in a minute she came back. "Where are you from?"

"Place called Pass Robin," I said.

She looked all of a surprise. "Why, I'm from there myself. At least, out in the country from Pass Robin. I'll just bet I've seen you on the street." She frowned between her eyes. "Though I don't see how that could be. I didn't hardly ever get to town."

During all this talk, of course, this other girl was on top of me, working away like she was the star of the show, and the new girl was lying beside me, another girl doing to her what these lesbians love to do.

At this moment, when it seemed like we didn't have nothing else to say to increase the acquaintance of two people from the same old home town, the girl left Him, so the new girl took her place. When she slid down on Him, it was like He remembered mightily that good cunt, because it did jerk Him to full attention. And there we were again, her face above my face, her eyes gazing into my eyes, and they were changing in color, going darker and darker, as her sweet little pussy started doing that surprising and wonderful thing.

I grabbed hold of her with my arms. But then I said, "Stop now, you're ruining me, damn it. I've got to finish the show."

"I can't help it," she said. "That's just the way I am."

It wasn't that she was fucking so hard. It was

just that her pussy was so alive! And I knew if I didn't get out of her. . . . But I didn't want out, I suddenly realized, even knowing I had to save Him.

I started to come. Her eyes went darker still, feeling it, and inside she was loving and stroking and loving and just eating Him up in little bitty bites. So I came all over her, once, and twice, and then three times, like I had never done it in my life. When I laid limp, she said, still not moving, "I'm sorry. I couldn't help it. I'm really sorry," and, so help me, tears stood in her beautiful eyes.

"Go away," I said, as mean as I felt like saying it, and without another word, she did.

It was the first time I'd ever had to fake it, there in the sex show or anywhere else, and I was ashamed of myself, having to keep my wilted cock hidden from the audience as I hurried off the stage before some old lady came down, to be disappointed by what she found when she got there.

The next afternoon, coming back from a photographer's studio, I ran into the new girl on Chartres Street. She was standing with her back to me, gazing into a window full of old clocks, but I recognized her right away. Feeling myself tighten inside, I started to go on by, but she happened to turn just then and saw me.

"Well, hello," she said in exactly the same tone as when I had first shoved Him into her sweet pussy.

"Hello," I said shortly, not breaking stride.

She came hurrying after me. "Don't be mad," she said. "I told you, I couldn't help it, didn't I?"

I didn't say anything. I didn't stop, either.

She was having to run to keep up with me. "You can't be mad at me, not when we're from the same home town."

Such a statement made me smile. So then there wasn't nothing for it but to stop and say, "All right, I won't be mad. But you did give me a hard time, you know."

She tossed her head and switched her ass. "Didn't want to be in that old show in the first place."

"Why?" I said curiously. "I don't mind it all that much. In fact, I sort of like it."

She cut an eye at me. "I don't feel right doing It unless I get paid."

Well, if she thought I had it in mind to spend a dollar, she had another think coming. She was a long way from being one of my old ladies. Young girls like that, they just don't interest me.

"But you're working there, after all."

She nodded seriously. "I know. I suppose it's getting paid, in a way. But . . . it don't *feel* like it."

"Yeah," I said. "I see what you mean. Now, me, I'm just the other way around. These old ladies are always trying to give me money, but I can't see my way clear to taking it, not and feel right with myself."

"How do you live, then?"

"By working in the sex show. How else? I get a hundred dollars a night. It's funny, I guess, but I don't mind that."

"You know what Miss Bascom charges to *see* the show? A hundred dollars a head. Just one customer pays your tariff."

"I don't care," I said. "I think it's plenty for what I do. Because I like standing up there with them looking at Him."

By now we had started walking along the street, moving very slowly as we talked, and stopping to look into the windows.

"What are you doing out?" I said. "Thought you girls slept all day."

She laughed. "I just like to get out and walk around when I can. So much to see in New Orleans, it's like a different city every day." She looked scornful. "Some of those girls, they don't set foot out of the house from one week to the next."

"You really are from Pass Robin? You weren't putting me on?"

"Near there. Out in the country." She sighed. "Seems a long way back, don't it?"

"Ain't no more than a hundred miles. You could take a Greyhound bus, be home in no time."

She shook her head. "Didn't leave nothing there I'd need to pay a visit to see." She looked at me. "What about you?"

"Me neither," I said. At which I thought about Billy. But I didn't say anything to her about Billy.

It did happen, though, that I did a strange thing; and I don't know to this day just why. We had come to a cross street, stopped, waiting for the light to change. When we made the step off the curb, I took her hand in mine.

We crossed the street hand-in-hand in that manner. Her palm was warm and smooth. When we reached the other side, though, she took her hand away, and ashamed of myself for having done it in the first place, I let it go. As we went on, there was a small space between us.

We had taken about half a dozen steps when she turned her head. "What's your name?"

"John," I said. "What's yours?"

"Alice," she said.

The Girl

The Captain's Paradise was just the nicest place I'd ever seen. A big old house, built square in three stories around this courtyard that had ferns and things growing in it, and a pretty fountain. The main room, where the customers met the girls, had dim lights and deep sofas and love seats, all red plush. A girl wasn't allowed to set foot in that room unless she was wearing an evening gown.

Among the dozen of us, you could choose just about any kind of woman a man could imagine. There was a black girl; a Chinese girl, like a cute little doll, you know, all yellow; and a blond—that was me and one other, except her blond wasn't real; and red-headed and blackheaded, and all. One was a full-blooded Indian, tall and thin; another was actually fat as a pig—she did the act in the show with the donkey, and we used to marvel at how she could manage such a big old Thing, at which she would

233

laugh her big laugh and say, "Girls, as you get older you'll find out that a cock is just a cock, no matter what it's hung on."

Nice girls to know, too; they taught me things that I hadn't known about, how to wash after the man was gone, and a better way to fix my hair, and helped me to decide on the style of my gowns. I had three, paid for in advance by Miss Bascom, but I'd have to work out their cost.

Miss Bascom herself was just the grandest person you'd meet in a lifetime. Though she could look and act as mean as a yard dog, she had this kindly streak that made her look after her girls like they were her very own daughters. There wasn't ever any rough stuff at the Captain's Paradise; she insisted on the highest type of customer, and got them, along with the best prices. Fine-looking men we served, prosperous and well-mannered. Many a man came only for a drink and good talk, with no idea of going upstairs, and would pay his tariff right on.

Upstairs was nice, too. The rooms didn't have numbers, but names; mine was called the Golden Harem, all got up in gold as to curtains and bedspread and fancy rug. To match my blond hair, I reckon, and my blue eyes. Taking a customer to your room was like entertaining, a lady and a gentleman together, not just stripping naked to let him take his pleasure. You were expected to furnish him a drink of fine whiskey, and carry on a conversation, everything to make him feel at home.

Miss Bascom, kindly though she was, was strict. She meant for us girls to be ladies if it killed us; never any coarse language, even in the mornings when no men were around. Every day, for an hour, she held a charm school, in which she taught us how to walk and sit, and how to converse, as she called it, in this nice low voice.

I felt so *safe* in the Captain's Paradise. All the

comforts of home, plenty of hot water and thick towels, and any man who set foot across the threshold knew how to treat a girl nice. Snake Dubois was no more than an ugly shadow in the back of my mind, to remember in the same breath with Papa taking my hard-earned money, and getting on me dog-drunk, to wind up crying because he had used his only daughter again. Miss Bascom had told me she would take care of Snake Dubois, and I knew in my heart that as long as I had her to back me up he would never again set foot in my life.

I had really and truly found my rightful place. It wasn't a week before I was the most called-for girl in the house. I was given the Golden Harem for my very own, which put some of the other girls' noses out of joint, let me tell you, and I was knocking down the highest price, because the minute Miss Bascom found out how special I was, she jacked it sky-high. At that, she wouldn't let me turn more than three tricks a night, because, as she said, it wasn't smart to make a great cunt cheap and easy. Before long, I knew three or four nights in advance who had booked me, and down in the main reception room I spent most of my time turning down customers, telling them they'd have to talk to Miss Bascom before they could hope to enjoy my favors.

I was making plenty of money again. Half of what I brought in was mine to keep, which, at my price, added up to more than the fifty dollars a man I had been earning out of Eddie's bar. So I was as satisfied with my life as I had ever been, the night Miss Bascom told me she would have to ask me to work in the sex show.

"I hate to do it, girl, you're so special," she said. "But with three girls out, there's no way around it, I'm afraid."

"Miss Bascom," I said, "when I came here, I didn't agree to work in no public shows."

235

She looked at me over her glasses. "This is an emergency," she said, her voice taking on a hard edge. "You will comply with my wishes."

"I won't," I said. "I don't see why I should make a public show of myself, and not get a dime for doing it, either."

"All the girls are paid twenty-five dollars," she said, sort of surprised. "They rather enjoy it, I must say. It makes a nice change."

"Well, I'm not interested in changing my luck," I said. "My three nice fellows a night, that's good enough for me."

"I'm sure you don't wish to go back to Snake Dubois, do you?"

I stopped. "You wouldn't do that."

She nodded firmly. "Disobedience is one thing I won't tolerate. Do as I say, or out you go." She softened it with a smile. "So be a good girl, dear, and let us be friends."

I'm stubborn, so I didn't give up on it, even though Miss Bascom had me by the short hairs; after knowing the Captain's Paradise, I'd never be able to go back on the street, to be hurt and hustled by the likes of Snake Dubois.

Yet it turned out to be just the nicest thing, because for the first time in all my travels, I got to meet a fellow from home.

Now, I'd heard the girls who worked the show talking about this boy, giggling and laughing amongst themselves. I had even viewed his performance, because sometimes one of my dates wanted me to watch with him before going upstairs to the Golden Harem.

A good-looking boy, I must admit; as blond as me, and elegant of build, with these nice stomach muscles and broad shoulders and narrow hips. I hadn't thought of him as the sort of person you'd want to get personally acquainted with, though, because he

236

was just too almighty proud of his old Thing. You could tell by the way he stood in the spotlight on that high stand and flaunted it. Seemed to me like that monster Thing there between his legs was the most there was to him, and he was satisfied with the situation.

Now, I'm not saying it wasn't a fine sample. Not only was it big and long and strong, but it was so clean and shining, and made so pretty, there was a sweet look to it, too, so that a woman, deep down inside herself, could think about love as well as the lust. I don't know if I'm putting it just right, because I'm so far different from those old women who seemed to follow him around, anxious to give It away, while I ... well, I had my pride, too, in knowing that I counted for as much in this world as any boy's old Thing, no matter how bright and shining and ready to be used.

Still, when I laid down on my belly to let him put his Thing into me, I got a pretty good surprise.

I think I can fairly say that I have made welcome many a man in my time, and it ain't often that I don't take pleasure as well as give it. I have taken the measure of large one and small ones, long ones and thick ones, strong ones and weak ones. There ain't no two alike, which is one of the nice things to know and experience.

But I've got to admit it. When he put that star Thing of his up into me, I fitted it like a glove. I can't remember when a man's Thing felt just so right, even though he was doing It dog fashion, which is not exactly my favorite way of fucking.

The minute I took it into me, I understood why he was the star of the show, why the artist Miss Bascom told about had desired to use it for a model.

Yes. I recognized his quality. Which was why I turned my head to smile and say, "Well, hello," because there ain't a jealous bone in my body. If there had happened to be a girl working the Captain's Paradise who was better at the trade than I was, I would have been the first to say it.

I could tell that he was pleasuring himself, too. After all, he had ahold of the best piece in the house, didn't he? And he recognized quality just as quick as I did. So I laid there, thinking to myself all over again, as I have done many and many a time, how wonderful it is in this world to get paid for doing what you like best of all. Don't many people, seems like, get to have that kind of luck.

When, all of a sudden, I realized that he was fixing to come, I wanted to feel it spurting into me, and got ready to bring it about. But at the last minute he jerked out, saving it, and when I turned, he gave me the most serious, hurt look you can imagine. Then, bless his heart, he smiled and nodded, and it was as good as a round of applause, because I understood what he was telling me. Which made me smile in return.

He kept on with the performance, and I took up my part. But, still curious where I had seen him, the first chance I had, I just up and asked. When I found out that he was from Pass Robin, it was the nicest surprise of all.

Mixed with that good feeling, and the sweetness I still felt from the first time, I was peeved that the boy hadn't let me do him good—along with, maybe, a smidgen of something else, watching him fuck the girls one after the other and then back off, looking pridefully up at the audience, his great hard still red and glowing and jerking greedily for more, letting them old women up there admire him, just holding their breaths and wetting their pants. I've got to admit it. By God, when I got my second chance at his old Thing, I meant to let him know he'd been fucked by somebody who was just as much of a champion as he was, and maybe a little bit more.

238

Sweet and friendly and a little bit of mean, all stirred up in me and showing its complicated self down there between my legs where it counted. I want you to know, from the first move he didn't have a chance. He didn't *want* no chance, he was gazing as deeply into my eyes as I was gazing into his, and he grabbed aholt with all arms and legs.

Oh, he tried. He even begged, saying, "Stop now, you're ruining me, damn it, I've got to finish the show."

If he can do his thing, I told myself, little old me can do mine; and let him know I was as great in my female way as he was in his male way. So I told him, "I can't help it, that's just the way I am"; and that was when he started to come.

It was the most glorious feeling of victory I've ever had when I felt him pumping his stuff hard into me; I could feel every drop, strong and scalding. I was too busy being the best in the world, though, to want to get excited myself. Oh, it moved once, way back in there, like it had done with Eddie's tongue, when I realized he didn't aim to quit coming for a while, now that he'd started. But, pushing it away, I wouldn't let myself think about it.

Then the strangest part of it all happened. The minute I realized he was done for good and all, knowing in my mind and in my body that I had whupped him down, making him to be a real man instead of a showpiece, I felt tears stinging my eyes, and I had to say, "I'm sorry, I couldn't help it. I'm really sorry."

Couldn't help it? When I had done it with full intention, out of sweetness and friendship and meanness and jealousy? So why did I have to say something like that? Yet, in a way I didn't understand, it was God's level truth. Not a lie in it.

When I ran into him on the street the very next day, I had nothing but the friendliest feelings. After all, he *was* a Pass Robin boy, and I was, practically speaking, a Pass Robin girl. So when he stalked right past me, I couldn't.stand it, but had to go after him. It took some doing to mollify his pride, all right, but I wouldn't give up, until finally we were strolling along chatting about our home town like lifelong friends.

He was so friendly and comfortable, by now, to be with, that at first it didn't bother me when he took my hand to cross the street. Then, all of a sudden, it flew all over me that here we were holding hands like high-school sweethearts. It made me hot and cold at the same time, and if he happened to glance at me, he'd know that I was blushing.

I snatched my hand away and moved a step to one side so we wouldn't be so close together, chiding myself that I had left myself open to any such doings. Never in my life had I walked hand-in-hand with a boy right out in public like that. My business and my interest was with grown men who had money in their pockets, and I hadn't yet run across a man like that who was interested in holding hands.

For some reason or another, I wanted to know his name. After that, still side-by-side, we walked on, though I felt so embarrassed with myself and with him that there didn't seem to be anything else to say. So when we came to the next corner, I stopped.

"I'd better get on back. Miss Bascom has got a busy night lined up for me, I'm afraid."

He looked at me very directly for a second before his eyes skittered away. "You do this very often?" His voice was tight and jerky, like he was having a hard time getting the words to speak themselves. "I mean . . . go walking in the French Quarter?"

"Just about every day," I said. "I like to get out of the house once in a while, just to be by myself."

He nodded very hard, agreeing with me a hundred precent. "I like to walk the streets, just looking at the people, studying the store windows." He ran out of words, and still he wasn't looking at me. Then he said, "Listen . . ." He cleared his throat. "Listen, next time you come out, tomorrow, I mean, we could have just a fine time. . . ." He was suddenly looking at me, having got up his courage. "I could meet you right here on this corner, anytime you say."

Well, I never! I took a step away. "I can't do that," I said.

"Why?"

I felt flustered all over again. "It just ain't right, lallygagging around in public like that." I tossed my head. "I'm just not that kind of a girl."

His voice was begging again. "People do it all the time," he said. "Nothing wrong with it. It's just friendly, being friends. . . ."

"Well, I don't," I told him haughtily.

He took a step to close the gap I had made between us. He reached out his hand. "Please, Alice. Please?"

I wouldn't let him touch me, but moved my arm away. Because it made something move inside of me to hear him begging so, I said hastily, "I've got to go," and nearly ran to get away from him.

Well, I told myself when I'd had time to calm down, that's that, and good riddance. Ain't it just like a boy to try to take advantage of a girl's friendly feelings just because they happen to come from the same town? Every time I thought about it, it made me mad all over again, until I put it out of my mind and wouldn't let my thoughts dwell on him anymore.

But let me tell you something which may be hard to believe. Feeling easy and comfortable with myself again, having made up my mind it'd be a month of Sundays before I'd show myself friendly to a fellow again, I went out for a stroll the very next day,

241

and before I had gone six blocks, I discovered that he was tagging along after me.

Yes, sir. Hangdog and determined. Every time I'd turn to look, he'd be again. I wasn't going to have any such, not for a minute. So I turned and marched myself back, to catch him fair and square, his face flaming red.

"What are you doing?" I demanded.

He seemed to have the hardest time looking me straight in the face. "Just walking around, seeing what there is to be seen."

I put my hands on my hips. "How is it that you have to do it in the same block I'm doing it in?"

He raised his eyes. I have never to my memory seen a man blush like that, fiery red and knowing it.

"Because I want to walk with you and be friends," he said.

It was just too much. All of a sudden I was laughing my fool head off at the silly idiot. He grinned, sheepish as all hell, and didn't know whether to get mad or be pleased.

"Ain't no harm in it," he said. "Not that I can see."

"Oh, hell and damnation," I said. "Come on, if nothing else will do you."

So we walked. And we talked. Not just that one time, either, but day after day, until it got to be a regular thing that we could count on. We talked about Pass Robin, and how strange it was to be out in the world making our own ways. He told me all about his life, and I told mine. Then he got to telling me his thoughts, which encouraged me to do the same, and when, one day, he took my hand again, I didn't have a reason in the world to say him nay.

Then, one day when we were down by the river, watching a freighter make its way out to sea, laying low and stately in the water, he turned to me and

242

said, "I ain't never told you, have I, Alice, that I was born a twin? Well, I was. Had a twin brother named Billy, who died of a fever when him and me were nine years old."

"No," I said. "You never mentioned it."

Part of the time he was looking at me, and part of the time he wasn't, but he held my hand throughout the telling about his twin brother and how they had been, one to the other. Then he wanted to tell me the rest of it, how he always had the feeling that Billy was with him—he even smiled, saying, "I know Billy likes you, too, Alice, I can just feel that he does" —but he couldn't seem to find the right words to make me know that ever since Billy had died, John felt like he had to live one life for himself, then another life for Billy, doing and feeling and being the things that Billy would have wanted to do and feel and be. I knew how important it was to him, though, because, holding his hand in mine, I could feel it get warm sometimes, and then turn clammy cold. So when he got to where he couldn't go on any longer, I told him what I felt about it all.

Leaning close, I said, "John, I think it's just wonderful."

He stared like he couldn't believe my words. "Do you think so?" he said uncertainly. "It isn't just a crazy idea in my head?"

"I *know* so," I told him.

His face tightened. "But it's so tough, Alice, sometimes I can't hardly stand it. Billy is dead, I know that, but at the same time, he's not dead, so I can't ever get over the grieving in my heart."

Already holding one hand, I took the other one, too. "But can't you see how wonderful it is, too? You've got something nobody else in the whole wide world has got, something that can't be lost, because nobody can take it away from you. If that ain't mar-

243

velous, I don't know what is." I felt my voice break. "Marvelous for him, too—Billy, I mean. I just wish I knew somebody would keep me alive in his heart after I'm dead, the way you keep Billy alive."

It was another wonder to see his face change on hearing my heartfelt words. "I . . . hadn't ever thought about it like that."

I gripped his hands hard. "Don't you see? You can't ever be alone, no matter where you go. I've been alone all my life, and let me tell you, it ain't no bowl of cherries. Why, you're the very first person I've ever been able to talk to, really and truly, in my whole life."

He looked at me, very solid and very deep. "Is that true, Alice? Is that how you really feel?"

"I wouldn't say it if it wasn't."

He smiled, just the sweetest smile I've ever seen on the face of a man. "Then I *am* something. Because I've got Billy, and I've got you."

"Well," I said, "I've got you, and because I've got you, I reckon I've got Billy, too. How about *that?*"

We both laughed. He stood up, dragging me to my feet. "Come on."

At that minute I would have followed him anywhere. He was hurrying, so it was hard to keep up. When we reached this place, and he turned up the stairs, though, I held back.

"What's up there?"

He was impatient. "This is where I live."

I drew back. "I don't . . ."

"All I want to do is show you a picture of me and Billy," he cried out. "It's the only one I've got that shows us both together."

I couldn't deny him, not after all he had told me. Still, I felt uneasy going right into John's living quarters like that.

He had a nice place, except there wasn't much of John to mark it as his own, only his clothes and such.

Looking about, I knew as plain as if he had told me that he didn't know *how* to make the place he lived a home. When he walked out of this room, or any other, it was left empty. With a shudder, I recognized the same failing in myself. What we had, or were, we carried with us, toting it on our backs like a hermit crab.

I sat down on the edge of the bed while he went rummaging into his drawers. He came to sit beside me, holding out the picture.

It was the kind of picture that gets taken in a booth at the county fair, or down at the public beach. The two boys were scrounged together, cramped by the space, both wearing sailor suits and both looking straight into the camera, laughing. The flash of the light had made their eyes white-rimmed, so that they looked startled.

I laughed at John. "You didn't have to show me this old picture to let me know what Billy looked like. All I had to do was look at you."

He smiled. "Most people couldn't tell the difference, sure enough. Used to be a regular game, fooling people, which was which." He stopped talking to look at the small picture. "But you *can* tell the difference. It's there as plain as can be."

I studied the picture. I studied him. "No difference, John. Because you're all he was, then, and all that you were. You're John and Billy both, and if there ever was a difference, it ain't there anymore."

He held out the picture at arm's length. Then he brought it up close. "Well, I'll be damned," he said. He turned to look at me. "That's nice, ain't it? Real nice."

"Yes," I said.

He had always felt it. Now, for the first time, he had seen it. It made him so happy I had to put my hand on his arm.

"You told me your real thing, so now I got to
245

tell you mine," I said. I looked away. "It ain't a nice, happy thing like you've got, though."

He didn't say anything, just waited until I was ready.

I held his arm hard with my hand. I could feel my fingernails digging into his flesh, so warm and real and close.

"The first man that ever had the using of me was my very own papa," I said into the empty spaces of the room. "He'd get dog drunk and do It to me, and every time I catch the smell of whiskey on a man's breath, it comes back on me. Every time."

He didn't say anything, I guess because there wasn't anything to be said; he just laid his arm across my chest, pushed me back on the bed, and laid down beside me. I turned to put my face into his shoulder. I could smell the good of his body, just so clean and fine.

"It wasn't just the once, it was the many," I said into his shoulder. I felt a shudder ripple through me. "And then he'd cry. He'd cry so hard it would have broke a body's heart to hear it if it hadn't been for the smell of that old whiskey."

"I ain't never took a drink of liquor in my life," he said. "I just don't like the taste of the stuff."

We laid there. And though what I had had to tell him wasn't the least bit nice, it turned out to be a nice thing after all. Because we didn't have to keep on talking about it, but could just lay there, him holding me, and me holding him.

After that long while, I felt the change in him, so that I was already moving before he put his hand on me, right down there between my legs.

On my feet, I said, "Now, just one darned minute! What do you think you're doing?"

He got up, his hands reaching for me. "Alice . . ."

I jerked away. "I ain't going to take no money from you. And I don't do It without getting paid."

246

He wasn't listening. He just came on, his arms closing to keep me from escaping. He started kissing my neck, his hands sliding down over my hips to hold me close. I could feel his old Thing stiff and strong inside his pants. I stood without moving. I wouldn't let myself answer.

Finally, knowing it wasn't any good, he stopped, letting go all holds. His face was hurt and bashful and bewildered.

"Alice, I ain't never had no use for a young girl. But . . . I got to. I just got to . . . Please, Alice."

"I said no, and I mean no."

I started walking toward the door. In another ten seconds I'd have been safely outside his old hermit-crab shell; but it was not to be. He came after me, catching and turning and lifting me, to drop me on the bed. Breathing hard, he stood looking down. Then, before I could make a move, he laid the full weight of his flesh on my flesh and held me pinned to the mattress.

I fought him. Oh, Lord, I did fight him. I'm strong, you wouldn't believe the strength that's in me, even though I ain't no bigger than a minute, but he was stronger, and he didn't care how hard I struggled to keep him from putting his old Thing where he meant to put it.

First, holding me down, he began kissing me, one hand on my breast, stroking the nipple with thumb and finger through the thin dress material. Wiggling and squirming, I kept turning my head from one side to the other to escape his mouth. But it seemed like, for every time I managed to avoid the kiss, there was a time when I felt his hot mouth.

Shifting to one side, he put that old hand of his under my dress again. Catching hold of my pants, in one move he just ripped them. They were the prettiest little blue pants a girl ever wore, too, embroidered with a rose where they needed to be, and it made me

247

mad, so that when he spread his hand into my crotch, I worked twice as hard to get away from his searching.

But he wouldn't be gainsaid, and feeling this dangerous heaviness in my flesh, I began to wear out with the fighting, until at last I quit struggling and let his hand do its will. Looking up into his face, I made my gaze hard and unforgiving, meaning to show him that he might be able, by main force, to do like unto that, but he couldn't expect a girl to like it.

Once I was still, he quit being so rough, but moved his hand slowly, gently, while he smiled down into my eyes. Then, his hand deep and true, he leaned his head to kiss me just as full and just as deep. All right, I told myself. He's got this far, so let him twirl it all he wants to. But he won't go no further, that's for sure.

Which was the way a girl ought to feel, I reckon, when she's been pushed so hard. But the next thing I knew, he had pulled his zipper to let his old Thing out of the cage and lay it, a steaming, throbbing rod, across the nakedness of my hip. And before I knew what he was up to, he put my hand on that old Thing.

I snatched away like it had been scalded. "No," I said. "No!"

That only served to start me all over again, thumping and thrashing under his weight, so desperate to get free I couldn't stand being held down another minute. He was riding the surges, laying flat on me from shoulders to ankles, his old Thing down between my legs but not finding the goodie hole, by God, not if I had anything to say about it.

I just about had it won. He was getting discouraged at the fight I kept putting up to save myself from such a fate; his old Thing had wilted, like it was sort of getting out of the notion too.

248

So I don't understand it. Any second, now, he'd give it up and let me walk out of there the girl I had been when I had come to his room. And I, by God, would make damn sure not to ever again get into the situation where he could wrestle me for It.

I didn't do it. I swear I didn't, because I was winning, wasn't I, I *had* won. So why was it that my legs opened and lifted, putting a fierce pressure into the small of his back that made his old Thing go deep and hard into me before either of us could catch our breaths?

That's what happened. And it hurt. I was cold inside, and it hurt like no man had ever traveled that sweet road. No man ever had, not without paying his tariff, except that bastard of a desk clerk, and the men Snake Dubois had sent me to to pass out freebies. And Snake himself, of course.

I couldn't blame this on Snake; I had taken John's old Thing of my own free will—or the free will of my flesh, at least. So it quit hurting as I felt myself melt, my body spreading and opening to take him deeper and deeper, so deep I wouldn't believe it, I could feel every throbbing inch, and he felt me, too, because when he touched bottom we both exploded. I was holding on with everything I had to hold on with. I was rocking with him, going with him and against him at one and the same time, and I was laughing and crying and hollering, raking at his shoulders with my fingernails.

It went on forever, until it was emptied out of him, and out of me, and I was so wet with his come, and mine, I felt like a warm sponge. We laid still, holding each other. Then I said, "Well, now you've done It, I just hope you're satisfied," and started crying.

I couldn't help myself. I had lost something I wouldn't get back again, I couldn't ever be the girl I had been, I'd have to be a woman now, for good and all. A girl has got to cry when that happens to her.

He didn't try to say anything; he just kissed the wetness of my eyes, very gently, and began moving in me with that same sweet way of feeling, his Thing, though half-limp now, so nice and good I could feel him a hundred times more truly than before, in all its greedy hardness. It was gone now, gone for good, so I might as well let him have his way. My way, too —I won't deny it. Because I started fucking up against him, not demanding anything, just slow and sweet, in tune with the deep waves rolling long and steady through my flesh, like the long waves that come into the Gulf beaches for days after a big storm has passed through, bringing up the funky smells of the ocean bottom.

When John came to it again, it was the same, starting deep, so far back I could only sense it at first, then coming on slow and good, and even at the end, when he pumped into me, it was still so gentle and loving and complete that it finished us; there wasn't nothing of loving each other that we could do anymore, for the time being.

Still and all, as we laid finished together, I felt this lost, empty place in my heart, a certain kind of sadness that I reckon a man can't ever know about; so that, when he took himself out of my body, I turned away, curling in on myself, weeping very softly and very quietly like I hadn't ever cried before in my life.

John did the right thing. He didn't ask anything else of me, just curled against my back, fitting himself from head to toe, and put one arm over to hold my breast in the palm of his hand.

I don't know how long it was before I finally sat up, snuffling and wiping at my face with both hands. Then, getting slowly to my feet, I picked up my pants, only to find them useless.

250

"You just ruined my pretty blue underpants," I said.

"I'm sorry," he said.

I looked at him, lying there buck naked on the bed for all to see, and he wasn't the least bit sorry, because there was this self-satisfied little smile marring his face. I dropped the pants and put on my dress, feeling myself so naked underneath I knew I'd be ashamed and embarrassed to walk down the public street.

"I've got to go now," I said.

He didn't say anything. In fact, he looked half-asleep already. It made me want to lay down beside him and curl up and go to sleep myself. Instead, I found my purse, took out a comb and a brush, and fixed my hair. I found my lipstick and put on just a little dab, smoothing it with my finger while looking in the hand mirror.

"I'm going now," I said.

"Come here and kiss me first," John said.

I went to lean over him. He put up one hand to take the curve of my neck while he gazed deep into my eyes. A sweet, lazy smile showed on his lips. I put my mouth on that smile and felt his lips move, tasting me. A lovely, friendly kiss, without need or passion.

I straightened, not wanting to ruin my lipstick all over again.

"I'll see you tomorrow," he said.

There wasn't a question in it. He didn't have to ask. I went to the door and opened it, turned to look at him naked on the bed.

"You ever tell anybody I let you do It for nothing, I'll kill you," I said. Then I went out.

But when he saw little Alice the next afternoon, it wasn't exactly what he was looking for, I tell you. Not by a long shot. I walked right on by

251

him, where he stood waiting on the corner, my head held high. He stood stunned for a minute, then hurried after me.

"Alice! What's the matter?"

I turned on him. "You've ruined me, that's all," I said furiously. "Ruined me for good and all, and I just hope you're satisfied!"

"But . . . but what . . . ?"

"I'll tell you what."

I was so mad I didn't care that people were passing by who could hear every word I had to say. He saved me from public shame, though, by grabbing my arm, saying, "Come on. We can't talk here."

I would have gone anywhere for the chance to let him know the hurt he had caused me. In his room, he wanted me to sit on the bed beside him, but I wouldn't. So he sat down, while I stood over him.

"All right," he said bravely. "How did I ruin you?"

I told him. In no uncertain terms.

Last night I had had a date with just about my favorite customer, a fine fellow indeed, prosperous and kind. Though he was a little soft in the stomach, he played a lot of golf, he told me, which gave strength and wind to his enthusiasm, so that, once or twice, I had actually had to hold hard to keep from losing control with him. He did fuck good. Besides all that, we were also good friends, and he never failed to give a twenty-dollar tip above and beyond what he owed the house.

This particular time, he had paid for the whole night. Which made me know that we'd be fucking till daylight, because when he got started, he didn't know how to quit. To start off, I did him nice with my mouth. Then he did me nice with his. Then, more than ready, he got into me. I was laying there, holding him, feeling his old Thing as busy as a churn paddle in me, and as far as I was concerned, everything was fine. But all of a sudden, he stopped.

I looked up, smiling a little. "What's the matter?"

"What's the matter with *you?*" he said.

I stirred, taking him closer and warmer. "Why, nothing's the matter with me. What are you talking about?"

"You've always been so alive, so . . ." He shifted impatiently. "You're dead tonight, dear. You're just not putting out."

The minute he spoke it, I knew the truth of his words. He might as well have been stirring me with a matchstick.

"I guess maybe I don't feel too good," I said uncertainly.

He shoved his old Thing hard and mean. "Well, come on, baby. You know what I pay my good money for. So get with it."

I tried. Not for him so much as for myself, because for the first time I could remember, I was ashamed of my performance. Because I knew, by now, what was the matter. It was not that John had taken anything away from me; actually, he had woke up something, sleeping all these years, that I hadn't even known was there. Changed so, I laid cold and lifeless to this other man's Thing; when I moved, it was because I *told* myself to move, *made* myself do it.

Now, that may be satisfactory for some girls who don't know any better. But it wasn't near good enough for little Alice. Alice had always known that she was the best ass in the world, bar none; not only had many a man told her so, she knew it in and of herself.

I couldn't admit that I had mislaid my talent so. I even tried to force myself into losing control, knowing that my customer would reap the benefit. When

253

I realized it wasn't working, I tried to fool my flesh, putting my mind on how it had been yesterday with John. No damned good. He stopped again, gazing down on me, this stony look to his eyes, and he wasn't my friend anymore.

"I didn't pay for a two-dollar whore, baby, but that's what I'm getting," he said harshly. "I might as well have it stuck into a bowl of cold oatmeal."

I turned my head, not able to say a word. So ashamed I could have died.

He jerked himself out of me and reached to press the button that he knew, as well as I did, would bring Miss Bascom on the run—it was put there in case some crazy fellow tried to give a girl a hard time.

I stopped talking. I looked John straight in the eye.

"When Miss Bascom got there," I said to John, "my customer told her flat out, 'I want another girl.'"

Miss Bascom looked at him. Then she looked at me. "What's the matter?"

He jerked his thumb at me. "Because she's a lousy lay."

Miss Bascom's eyes were like needles as they studied me. "You've always bragged that she was the best girl you've ever had," she said.

He made a short laugh. "Not tonight. Tonight she's cold enough to freeze a man's cock off. I want my money's worth."

She smiled at him. Keeping the customer happy. "Put on your pants and come with me." She was still smiling. "How about a nice Chinese piece? She's got tricks you won't believe."

"So he left," I told John bitterly. "The first customer I've ever had to go away dissatisfied. He didn't even say good-bye."

"And then," I told John. "Miss Bascom came back."

I was sitting on the side of the bed, shoulders slumped, when I looked up to see her standing in the doorway, looking daggers.

"What's the matter, girl?"

"I don't know," I said hopelessly. "I just don't feel good, I reckon."

"Feel good?" she said, her voice rising a notch. "You're a pro, aren't you? With an important client like that, you can't bother about whether you *feel* good or not. A real pro, if she can't feel it, she can fake it. The john will never know the difference."

"I ain't never faked It in my life."

Her voice beat at me like fists. "You'd better learn. And quickly. If you don't want to look Snake Dubois in the face again."

I felt myself trembling. But, so ashamed, so hurt with myself, I couldn't even rise to that threat.

She softened her tone. "Girl, you're the best whore this house has presented to its clientele in its entire history. They all tell me that. You're the star of the Captain's Paradise; that's why I keep you scarce and make you expensive. So get with it, girl! You've got it all, and you don't want to lose it. Why, with your saving ways, you can retire a wealthy woman; you'll be fixed to open your own house, if you want to, when you get tired of fucking."

I looked at her, tears brimming in my eyes. "I'll try, Miss Bascom."

Her voice got hard again. "You'll have to do better than try," she said grimly. "One more complaint, you'll find yourself on Bourbon Street, working for Snake Dubois. I must maintain the standards of the Captain's Paradise. Once you set a new standard, you must keep it up. Or . . . out you go. Understand?"

I nodded miserably. "I understand."

I said bitterly to John, "So you see how you've

255

ruined me? You wouldn't be denied of having me for nothing, you practically raped me, and now you've cost me my trade."

He didn't say anything. I had expected him to become angry in return, maybe to apologize, at least to kiss me and say he was sorry. But he just sat looking down at his hands, a curious smile on his face.

He raised his eyes to mine. "The same thing happened to me," he said quietly. "Went to a new old lady last night, just the finest lady you'd ever expect to meet." He stopped. Then he went on. "I got Him up, all right, because she was just all over me. I even got Him into her. But then . . . He died."

He reached to unbutton his shirt. "I thought she was going to kill me. Look."

There were angry long scratches down his chest; bite marks scarred his smooth skin. He looked like he'd been clawed and chewed by a wildcat.

His face showed misery. "She was so mean about it, too. Said certain lady friends had been bragging about me so, how great I was, she just made up her mind to find out for herself. She found out, all right, she told me. Found I couldn't even keep Him up long enough for a lady to begin to get warm. Then she made me watch while she fingered herself. After she'd had all of that she could stand, she threw me out of the house."

He stopped. We were both the picture of misery. "So I reckon you ruined me, you made me a one-woman man," he said. "Just like I ruined you."

I felt my heart moved, so that, going close, I touched the deepest mark on his chest with one gentle finger.

He put his arms around my waist, holding so tight I could hardly breathe. "There's not but one thing for it," he said.

"What's that?" I said, hope growing in me.

He held me out at arm's length to gaze into my

eyes. "We've got to keep each other," he said. "We're all we've got now."

For a long minute we looked at each other. Then I said, "Fuck me. Oh, God, John, fuck me."

He did.

Afterward, he said the other thing, like he had thought of it when nobody else ever had before. "We ought to get married."

I rolled over on my stomach to look at him. "We don't have to do that."

"Yes," he said. "We do. Will you marry me?"

I thought about it. "Yes," I said quietly. "I will. But . . ."

He tightened his arms. "But what?"

"Miss Bascom . . ."

"She'll be all right," John said confidently. "Miss Bascom is a kind lady." He stirred. "You don't want to work there anymore anyway, do you?"

"Want to or not, I can't," I said pertly. "You fixed that."

He nodded soberly. "Yeah. So she won't mind, I'm sure, once she comes to understand how it is."

Well, John had been dead right up to that point, and I had been dead right. But that's exactly where we started to go wrong. Because Miss Bascom minded so bad she could just taste the bitter of what we were telling her. She heard us out, sitting in her private suite at the Captain's Paradise, which hardly any of the girls ever got to see. The rooms were like Miss Bascom herself—strict but tasteful and very plain, not at all like the rest of the house.

She looked at me. She looked at John. "You are a pair of fools," she said bluntly. "Alice is the finest whore it's ever been my privilege to offer my clientele. You, John, are the best stud, and the greatest sex-show attraction. I won't let you quit. Either of you."

"I ain't no stud," John said. "Ain't never been. I just—"

257

Miss Bascom's voice picked up the tone of his voice. "—you just like to be kind to your nice old ladies." She stopped, her eyes hard and bright. "Don't kid yourself, boy. You've always been a stud, and you always will be."

John shook his head stubbornly. "No. I'm not. So I can quit anytime I want to."

She stared at him. Then she got up and went to a safe that stood against one wall. Standing so we couldn't see, she worked the combination lock. When she came back, it was to place a wad of bills on the coffee table before John.

"There's your share of the take," Miss Bascom told him. "I'm an honest woman, John. I've been holding your share of the money until you got good sense."

John looked at the money. He looked at her. His face was a study. "You mean . . . you've been charging my ladies?"

She laughed. "Of course. That's why I insisted you keep your phone number unlisted. You've been knocking down the same price as your little friend here. And worth every dollar." Her mouth quirked. "Of course, being so stupid about yourself, you managed to sneak one or two past me . . . and just this morning I had to refund the full price to a lady who was very upset with her experience."

John couldn't quit looking at the money. "You oughtn't to have done that to me, Miss Bascom."

"*To* you?" Miss Bascom said. "I did it *for* you. The money is yours. Pick it up and put it in your pocket. And let's don't have any more of this nonsense about quitting to marry this girl. Nobody marries a whore, don't you know that?"

John stood up, leaving the money laying there. "I'm going to," he said. "We . . . we hoped it would sort of please you."

"It doesn't," Miss Bascom said in a hard voice.

She switched her eyes to my face. "This girl shall not leave this house."

I leaned forward. "I can't do it anymore, Miss Bascom," I said, begging her to understand. She was a woman, I was a woman, she ought to be able to know what I was talking about. "Oh, I can lay there and let them poke their old Things into me from now to Sunday. I reckon any woman can do that much. But . . . I can't be what I was. And anything less just ain't good enough."

Her stern face didn't answer to my plea. She just stared at me for a full minute, her eyes black and pinpointed. Then she said, "I'd better get Snake Dubois in on this," and reached to pull the telephone closer.

A thrill of fear shot through me like electricity. She had the number halfway dialed before I could move. I don't know how I managed to make myself do it. But I reached over and broke the connection.

"What's he got to do with it?" I said.

Her voice was malicious with the words. "He still owns you, girl. Snake's been taking his share of your action ever since you came to the Captain's Paradise. Did you know that?"

I looked at John. He was looking at me. I could see in his face what he must be seeing in mine.

"But . . . but . . ." I said. My voice kept stumbling over the words. "Miss Bascom, you saved me from him. You . . ."

She actually laughed. "You think I *saved* you from Snake Dubois? Well, that's just marvelous." She sobered. "I suppose, in a way, I *did* save you. Because Snake, being the kind of pimp he is, would have beat you down to a two-dollar hump within a year." She regarded me curiously. "Did you really think Snake gave you up as easily as that?"

I nodded dumbly.

259

She chuckled. "You're as innocent, in your way, as your boyfriend is in his. Just a pair of babes in the woods." She nodded firmly. "I talked to Snake, convinced him he had a gold mine there between your legs if you were handled properly. He didn't like the idea of allowing me to manage you, but I told him that a girl with your spirit and your natural genius would only be ruined by his tactics. Finally he decided he liked money better than beating on you. After all, he's got plenty girls he can whip-ass on, but like I told him, you were one in a million. So . . ." She smiled slowly. "He's been coming around every Sunday morning, regular as clockwork, to pick up his profits."

"Oh, my God," I said softly. "If I'd known . . ."

"That's why you didn't know," Miss Bascom said briskly. "Now." She pulled the phone toward her again. "Snake will straighten you out, but good. Either you work in my house—and I mean work the way I know you *can* work—or back you go. There's no two ways about it."

She was dialing again. I looked at John. He looked at me. In the times we had talked together, I had told him all about Snake. So he knew how I felt in this minute, realizing that during all this fine time at the Captain's Paradise I'had been Snake Dubois's slave right on. He knew the terror that lived in me, waiting for the evil man, in just a few minutes, to come walking into this room, and into my life again. I had been living in a fool's paradise, instead of the Captain's Paradise.

"Wait a minute," John said.

Miss Bascom said into the telephone. "This is Miss Bascom. Is Snake there?" She listened. "Tell him to get back to me as quickly as possible. It's very important that I talk to him."

"Wait a minute," John said.

Miss Bascom put down the telephone. "Well?"

"Listen," John said rapidly. "Maybe we ought to think about this."

"Maybe you should."

He looked at me, only for a second. "Maybe you're right. We ought to keep on with what we're best at. Both of us, I mean. We could still be together, we could even get married if we wanted to. You wouldn't care about that, would you, Miss Bascom, as long as we kept on working?"

"Now, wait a minute," I said.

His little speech cheered Miss Bascom. "Why, John, I think that's a fine idea." She smiled upon him in the kindest manner. "I'll even give you your wedding, right here in the Captain's Paradise. The girls would just love the idea of a wedding." Her smile turned evil. "Maybe we can talk Snake Dubois into giving the bride away."

"Now, just one darned minute," I said. "I don't aim to—"

John whirled on me. "Shut up, Alice."

It made me furious. "Don't tell me to shut up!"

His voice got even in tone. "Either I'll shut you up, or Snake Dubois will. Now, which do you want?"

I died inside to hear him talk like that. Like any man you *give* It to, he thought he owned me now. There wasn't a word left in me, though, to throw at him.

"You're not thinking of cutting yourself in on her action, are you?" Miss Bascom said suspiciously. "Snake won't stand still for a three-way split. Nor will I."

He grinned at her. Yes, he actually grinned, the two of them as thick as thieves. "I'll have my own action going, won't I? So why should I take offen her?"

Miss Bascom nodded approvingly. "Now you're talking sense."

"I . . ." I said.

He grabbed me by the arm. Hard. "Don't worry, Miss Bascom, I'll get Alice's head straight. Come on, Alice, let me explain how nice it'll be, me and you together, yet still raking in the big money."

"Listen to him, girl," Miss Bascom said. "If he can't convince you, Snake Dubois surely can."

"Come on, Alice, let's take a walk," John said urgently. He was pulling on my arm to get me started off cold dead center.

"Be back by six, now," Miss Bascom warned. "I've got a busy night lined up for Alice. I know we've set a limit of three, but this one client, he's leaving town tomorrow for a while, so I promised him."

"She'll be home on time," John said. "I'll see to it."

He started to take me out of there. But Miss Bascom, standing up, said, "You're forgetting your money, John."

He seemed uncertain what to say to that, when he had been so sure of himself since him and Miss Bascom had got into cahoots. Then he said, "The only money I want is what I've earned when I know that I'm earning it. You keep that, Miss Bascom, and we'll start clean. All right?"

At that, I found myself able to talk. And move. I snatched up the bills, saying, "No you don't, John. You earned it by the sweat of your brow, and it's yours."

I looked at Miss Bascom. She nodded. "Don't let your man be any more foolish than you are yourself."

John was so anxious to get moving, he didn't stop to argue. He just dragged me outside, and once in the street, started walking so fast I could hardly keep up. He kept looking over his shoulder, too, and every corner we came to, he turned a different way.

When he finally stopped, he was panting; I

was out of wind. "What's the rush?" I said when I could.

"We had to get out of there before Snake Dubois called back."

I trembled again. "Yes. But . . ." Bracing myself, I looked him square in the eye. "If you think for one minute you're going to talk me into fucking anybody but you from now on, you've got another think coming."

"Don't be a silly fool," he said tenderly. "Didn't you catch on? Alice, we're getting out of this town. Right now. We're going home to Pass Robin."

It took my breath away. "John!"

He smiled. "We'll be safe in Pass Robin. From Snake Dubois. From Miss Bascom. From the whole damned dirty world."

"But . . ." I hesitated, looking back the way we had come. "All my pretty clothes, my . . ."

"Forget your clothes," John said strongly. "Set foot in that house again, you'll never leave it. Except maybe to go to work for Snake Dubois."

I shivered. "Yes. I . . ." I tightened myself again. "There's one thing I don't aim to leave, not for a minute. My money."

Dismayed, he stared at me. "You'll *have* to leave it, Alice. We can't take the risk of going back, not even for a minute."

"It's not there," I said triumphantly. "I've got all but a few dollars put away into the savings and loan."

His face cleared. "Wonderful! We'll have to hurry, though." He looked worried again. "Does Miss Bascom know where you've got it?"

"Don't nobody know," I said happily. "I reckon I can tend to my own business."

I'm a careful girl, so I not only turned my savings into traveler's checks, I made John do the same with his money. A girl has got to look after herself in this world; won't nobody do it for her. Except maybe a fine fellow like John, who's got love in his heart.

So it was that we turned our backs on the Captain's Paradise, never to see it again in this world, and set out for home.

John and Alice

Because they were so utterly terrified of Snake Dubois, John and Alice dared not risk the bus station. Instead they took a city bus to the outskirts and walked down Highway 90 East, hitchhiking as they went. They did not yet believe in their freedom, so it took much courage to stand exposed on the highway begging for a ride. Seeing a black limousine approaching slowly, they turned simultaneously to run behind a nearby service station. Forever afterward, in their souls, they believed their escape had been just that narrow.

Finally, an old pickup truck stopped for them. Since the cab was occupied by a farmer and his wife, they had to ride in the back. Rattling down the highway, they remained vulnerable to the passing traffic, even though sitting deep in the bed of the truck and facing forward.

Because of the late start, they didn't get far the

first day. When their second lift had come to an end, night was already upon them. Intent on putting distance between them and their enemies, John and Alice began walking, keeping to the side of the road, covering their eyes against approaching headlights. Going single file, Alice was constantly aware of John's back, strong and broad in the darkness. Occasionally she reached out to touch him.

At the outskirts of a small town, the familiar sign of a Holiday Inn beckoned. Alice said, "John?" but John replied, "We'd better not risk it."

"All right," Alice said.

Because they felt it exceedingly dangerous to walk through lighted streets, from an all-night service station they summoned a taxi by telephone. Paying off the driver on the other side of town, they pretended to have arrived at a friend's house. After the uninterested taxi driver had safely departed, they plodded onward. Soon they were again in the country. Late now, the traffic was sparse, so they no longer attempted to hitchhike.

Finally Alice stopped. "I don't think I can make it much farther, John," she said wearily.

John turned to take her into his arms. "We've got to keep going," he said, "Besides, if we lay out to sleep, the mosquitoes will just eat us alive."

Alice pointed to the lights of a farmhouse down the road. "See if they'll let us stay there. That would be safe enough."

"I guess so," John said dubiously. "I'd rather keep traveling."

They walked hand-in-hand into the yard, pausing when they saw the old couple sitting in the darkness of the screened front porch.

"Hello," Alice said, her voice tremulous.

"Howdy," the old man said. "What can we do for you?"

"We were wondering if you all could let us have a bed for the night," John said. "We've just been newly married, and we're trying to get home to our folks. But the dark caught us."

The old man rose stiffly and flipped on a porch light.

"We ain't got much money, but we'd be glad to pay," Alice added.

They stood holding hands while the old man and his wife regarded them. Finally the old woman said thoughtfully, speaking the words into the air rather than addressing them to her husband, "There's that back bedroom. All I'd have to do is put sheets on."

The old man turned his head toward her. "I don't know," he said. "All these hippies, like they call themselves, rambling the countryside, ain't no telling what devilment they're up to."

"These ain't hippies," the old woman said. "Why, look at them, they're just as clean and nice as can be, both with that pretty white hair and all. Neither one wearing it long, either." She smiled. "They do make a nice young couple, don't they?"

"It'll be a dollar," the old man said. He cleared his throat to amend it. "A dollar apiece, I mean."

"That'll be just fine," Alice said gratefully.

The old woman bustled hospitably out of her rocking chair. "Well, come on in, then, and make yourselves at home." As they came up the steps, the old man holding open the screen door, she said, "Did I hear you say you're newlyweds? Now, that's downright nice, couple of nice-looking young folks like you all getting ready to start in life together and raise a family."

While the old lady showed them the back bedroom and hurried to put on starched sheets, Alice, helping her, had to tell all about how they had been married yesterday in New Orleans and had spent nearly all their money on a wedding night at the Roosevelt Hotel, and that's why they had to hitch-hike home.

"That's just wonderful," the old woman said, beaming. "The Roosevelt Hotel! It's something you'll remember all the days of your life." She paused. "Have you et yet?"

The moment she mentioned it, both John and Alice realized they were ravenous. John said fervently, "No, ma'am, we sure haven't."

So they sat at the kitchen table and answered the old man's inquiries about John's future prospects, now that he had taken on the responsibilities of a family man—John assuring him he didn't worry his head none about that, because he had always been able to turn a dollar when needed—while the old woman warmed up leftover pot roast and turnip greens and dished up cornbread and poured sweet milk to go with it.

The moment they had finished eating, they were sleepy, so, making their excuses to the smiling under-standing of the old couple, they went quickly to bed. John wanted to make love, but Alice, feeling shy in her newly acquired status of bride, was sure the old couple would be listening shrewdly for the squeak and thump of bedsprings. So they merely held each other as they dropped tiredly off to sleep.

The new day brought new and shining luck. After a huge breakfast of eggs and bacon and toast and grits and coffee and scads of homemade jam—the old man refused payment for the food, accepting only the two dollars for the bed—they went out to the highway and in five minutes had caught a ride on a milk truck that took them miles along the way. After they were set down by the milk truck, a prosperous traveling salesman in a green Mercedes-Benz took them the rest of the way.

He would have deposited them in the heart of Pass Robin had not Alice suddenly said, before an approaching crossroads, "This is where we get off."

John, puzzled, glanced toward her, but she squeezed his hand, signaling silence. Only after the Mercedes had departed did she explain.

"Can you be sure you never mentioned to anybody where you came from?" she asked John.

"I don't *think* I did."

"Better not risk Pass Robin, just the same. I *know* I never told a soul in New Orleans where I was raised. So I reckon we ought to stay with Papa for a while, just to be safe." She pointed. "It's on down that road yonder."

"But your papa . . ."

She tossed her head. "Besides, I want him to know I'm getting married," she said. "A girl's got a right to tell her own papa good news like that, ain't she?"

John laughed at her. "I reckon so," he said. "Let's go."

When they turned into the narrower road that would be their last miles, Alice moved closer to John and put her arm around his waist. They walked slowly, in step, their bodies touching in the rhythm of walking. They were both handsome young people, made infinitely more so by being so very much together. The girl was no bigger than a minute, her miniature body perfect in its loveliness. The boy, broad-shouldered and lean-hipped, not overly tall but strong and utterly masculine, was her perfect match. They were bright and shining youth, going unafraid into their paired future.

So John and Alice came home from their adventures, these two enormous I's so unconquerable in their great innocence that they returned as pristine, as unblemished, as ever. Yet there was change; though their

269

towering I's had, for individual reasons, shown themselves capable of savoring the egos that had impacted upon their egos, cherishing the stranger I's as they cherished their own, adapting to them, giving generously of their strength-of-innocence to all they met, they had also encountered twinned evils as strong as their twinned hearts. So, at the end, they had retreated into themselves, and because, having found each other, they were not alone, they had conquered even in strategic retreat.

It was Alice who said it. Tried to say it. As they walked with arms twined about each other's waists, she asked John shyly, "Are you happy?"

He smiled down at her. "Yes. Are you?"

"Of course." She sighed. Then, even more shyly, "Billy . . . is he happy?"

"Oh, God, yes," John said fervently. "Can't you tell?"

"Yes," she said quietly. "Because you ain't just you anymore, John, and I'm not just me. You're me and I'm you, and you're Billy and I'm Billy, so that we'll have to call ourselves We from now on, not just a couple of I's." She laughed shyly. "Because I'm your old Thing, and you're my sweet pussy, and so it's us and you and me and her and him . . ."

She stopped the fast run of talk, laughing again in puzzlement and delight. "Do you know what I mean?"

"No," he said. He squeezed her waist. "But I know. I do know."

"I don't know what I mean, either," she said. "But it's all right. I never had to depend on my head to get along in the world, anyway."

When they came to the artesian well, Alice paused. "Right there's where I turned my first trick," she told John in shy pride. Then, laughing softly at the girl she had been, she added, "For a quarter. A whole brand-new shiny quarter."

He laughed at her. "Worth every penny of it, too, I bet."

She hit him with her tiny fist. "I never done a man bad in my life. But just that once. And you know why that was."

John started on, but Alice hung back. "Wait a minute. Let's get a drink of water."

They drank, Alice first and then John, of the water coming cool and secret from deep in the earth. Then, taking his hand, Alice led John into the grove of trees. Pausing to look about, she remembered. With pride. With understanding of the girl she had been, of the woman she had become when John had entered her body for the first time.

She looked at John with that special signal, in her eyes and mouth, in the stance of her body.

"Fuck me, John. Oh, God, please fuck me."

Lifting her up tenderly, he laid her down on a bed of green moss beneath a water oak. There, on the sweet earth of home, he made love to her with all his genius of knowing what a woman needed and wanted, even the style in which she desired to receive it; while she responded with her equal genius of reading a man. As they fucked, Alice spread and opened, deeper and deeper, as she had never done with anyone but Him, and John was both fierce and gentle, demanding and giving, as he had never been with his old ladies. When he had flooded her with his sperm, not once but twice and three times, they lay together, still joined and never to be put asunder, as Alice gazed lovingly into his loving eyes, knowing, accepting, the miraculous thing happening inside her body, where he still lay thick and warm in their twinned juices.

When they went on at last, it was only to find the house where she had lived standing deserted, with that unmistakable emptiness of a house no longer waiting for the return of human beings. Alice insisted

271

on going on to the crossroads store. She went in alone to inquire; coming out again, she showed John a grief-stricken face.

"Papa's dead, John," she said in a low voice. "He put a shotgun to his head not more than a month after I left home." Her mouth trembled. "I never knew. I never felt it. I ought to have known, seems like."

He took her into his arms to comfort her grief. Not knowing what else to do, they returned to the empty house, not to enter, but to sit on the porch steps while she talked tenderly of her father.

Finally John said, "But he done you mean, didn't he? You told me . . ."

"He was still my papa!" Alice flared. Her voice broke. "He's gone, and I won't ever have no papa in this world evermore." John, knowing there were no words, held her close. After a time she stirred. "When your papa is gone, ain't nobody can take his place." She put her hand to her face, wiping away the tears. "But he's dead and buried, ain't he? By his own choice." She smiled tremulously. "He won't never know that I come home to get married. He won't never know his grandchild."

She looked up at John. "Because I'm pregnant now, you know. You knocked me up down there at the artesian well a while ago."

"It's too early to tell!" he protested.

She stood up. "I know." She touched her belly. "It's starting to grow. Right now."

He stood up beside her. But she did not touch him as she told him the rest of it. "My baby has got to be born right here where I was born. So we'll stay until then. We've got the money, plenty of money. Besides, I know Snake Dubois and Miss Bascom"—her body shuddered—"can't find us here."

John looked dubiously at the old house. "But . . ."

"Once we've got the baby, we can move into Pass Robin. But not before."

272

He looked at her. "All right. If that's how you want it."

She nodded. "That's how it's got to be." She laughed then, Alice coming back to herself out of grief and homecoming, into this new love that was brighter and shinier than any quarter she had ever earned proudly with her proud flesh. "Which do you want it to be?"

John thought for a minute. "A girl. A pretty little girl no bigger than a minute, just like you."

"No," she said firmly. "It's got to be a son. A boy that's the spittin' image of you and Billy."

Both wishes were granted—a twin boy and a twin girl, blond-haired and blue-eyed; and together they were as pretty as a picture. Soon afterward, the family moved into Pass Robin, where John and Alice bought out Old Man Adams and went into the grocery business for themselves. Except that John never made deliveries, hiring boys for that job, but devoted himself to waiting on the customers, cutting the meat, stocking the shelves.

Alice presided over the cash register.

And so they lived in reasonable happiness for a very, very long time.

HER

Anonymous

Rarely in the history of book publishing has a love story been told with the frankness and earthy honesty of *Her*, the adult love story that explores the lust, the passion, the ecstasy and the longing between a woman and a man – a book that portrays the beauty, the joy and the truth to be found in sensual love.

£1.50

HIM

Anonymous

After *Her* there could only be *Him* . . .

Every man and every woman contain two beings: the animal and the human; the spiritual and the bestial. Only when the two come together can a man or a woman experience true, sensual, ecstatic love.

Him is the story of two women and one man, who together shared a love affair that awakened them to a new world of carnality and lust – and that freed the primitive, sensual self of each.

£1.50

BESTSELLERS FROM ARROW

All these books are available from your bookshop or newsagent or you can order them direct. Just tick the titles you want and complete the form below.

A CHOICE OF CATASTROPHIES	Isaac Asimov	£1.95
BRUACH BLEND	Lillian Beckwith	95p
THE HISTORY MAN	Malcolm Bradbury	£1.60
A LITTLE ZIT ON THE SIDE	Jasper Carrott	£1.25
EENY MEENY MINEY MOLE	Marcel A'Agneau	£1.50
HERO	Leslie Deane	£1.75
TRAVELS WITH FORTUNE	Christine Dodwell	£1.50
11th ARROW BOOK OF CROSSWORDS	Frank Henchard	95p
THE LOW CALORIE MENU BOOK	Joyce Hughes	90p
THE PALMISTRY OF LOVE	David Brandon-Jones	£1.50
DEATH DREAMS	William Katz	£1.25
PASSAGE TO MUTINY	Alexander Kent	£1.50
HEARTSOUNDS	Marth Weinman Lear	£1.75
LOOSELY ENGAGED	Christopher Matthew	£1.25
HARLOT	Margaret Pemberton	£1.60
TALES FROM A LONG ROOM	Peter Tinniswood	£1.50
INCIDENT ON ATH	E. C. Tubb	£1.15
THE SECOND LADY	Irving Wallace	£1.75
STAND BY YOUR MAN	Tammy Wynette	£1.75
DEATH ON ACCOUNT	Margaret Yorke	£1.00
	Postage	————
	Total	————

ARROW BOOKS, BOOKSERVICE BY POST, PO BOX 29, DOUGLAS, ISLE OF MAN, BRITISH ISLES

Please enclose a cheque or postal order made out to Arrow Books Limited for the amount due including 10p per book for postage and packing for orders within the UK and 12p for overseas orders.

Please print clearly

NAME ....

ADDRESS...

....

Whilst every effort is made to keep prices down and to keep popular books in print, Arrow Books cannot guarantee that prices will be the same as those advertised here or that the books will be available.